PATIENT OR PERSON

PATIENT OR PERSON

LIVING WITH CHRONIC PAIN

Penney Cowan
Founder, American Chronic Pain Association

Foreword by EDWARD C. COVINGTON, M.D.

GARDNER PRESS, INC.
New York   London   Toronto   Sydney

The names, hometowns, marital status, and other personal
details of all the patients on the pain unit, as well as all other
patients at the Cleveland Clinic, have been changed to protect their identity. All other characters are real. The events
during my stay at the Clinic are true.

Gardner Press, Inc.
19 Union Square West
New York, New York 10003

Library of Congress Cataloging in Publication Data

Cowan, Penney.
    Patient of person : living with chronic pain / Penney Cowan.
        p.   cm.
    ISBN 0-89876-186-7
    1. Cowan, Penney — Health.   2. Intractable pain — Patients —
United States — Biography.   3. Cleveland Clinic Foundation. Pain
Management Unit.   I. Title.
    RB127.C73   1991
616'.0472'092—dc20
    [B]   91-25980
                                                            CIP

9   8   7   6   5   4   3   2

In loving memory of my father, Robert Silknitter

CONTENTS

ACKNOWLEDGMENTS

Where does one begin, when there are so many people to thank? I do not think I would have been successful in my attempt to find an end to my pain if it had not been for the love and support of my husband, Scott.

Both Dr. Edward Covington and Dr. Joseph Gabis played a very important part during my time on 7-B. If they had not been so supportive and understanding, believing in me until I could believe in myself, I would not have made the progress I did.

There are no words to describe the kind of devotion Deb Porter gave to me during the most difficult time of my life. She remained true to me and has become a very important part of our entire family.

The staff of 7-B gave of themselves in an effort to help me make the long and hard journey from patient to person. I thank them. I must add one more person, without whom, this book would not have been: Charles Lidz, Ph.D. It was his encouragement and belief in me that helped me continue this project long after I felt unable to see it to its completion.

PREFACE

Patient or Person is a daily account of my stay on a pain unit. During the time I lived in one of the country's leading medical centers, I was ashamed-the pain unit was on the psychiatric ward. Unbearable pain had been my constant companion since the birth of my second child. For six years I suffered with pain. Eventually, this pain controlled my life. There was not a move made or a plan laid where I did not first consider my pain.

I had gone to countless doctors hoping they would provide me with some relief. At first they used a variety of tests to determine what was causing the pain. Once it was clear that I indeed had chronic pain, pain that would never go away, pain that might not get any worse, but was not life threatening, they began treatment with drugs, forever urging me to: "learn to live with it." I tried their drugs and I tried to live with the pain, without success.

So I entered the Cleveland Clinic pain unit, where I underwent a complete metamorphosis. For the first time in my life I was forced to dig deep within myself in order that I might find out who I was. What did my personality have to do with the tremendous pain I suffered? Everything!

That is what this book is about. For seven weeks of my life I learned more about myself and my needs than at any other time prior to that. Feelings I had been denying began to surface. Images of loved ones were shattered. I even questioned my own sanity.

I hope my personal victory with chronic pain will help the estimated 86 million Americans who suffer from this affliction strive to become people as they leave the patient role behind.

FOREWORD

This is the story of one person's battle with chronic pain and her treatment in a pain management unit. It addresses the question of what one does when life has come to a halt because of unending pain and a succession of competent physicians confess their inability to solve the problem.

It confirms that healing is not the same as cure and is not contingent on finding remedies. It may, however, be contingent on connectedness with others. This is a story of trust, derived not from proof that others are reliable, but from a recognition that the risks of wariness are greater than those of trust. It is about overcoming fear and overcoming the self-especially that part of the self compelling one to respond to pain with regression, retreat, and inactivity.

In some ways the epilogue is as interesting as the story itself. Penney was fortunate to belong to a church that provided her and her family with support during the time she was unable to function because of her chronic pain. On completion of her treatment, she addressed the congregation to express her gratitude to them. Fatefully, there were listeners who also had chronic pain and who could see that Penney had undergone a transformation. (A common surprise in patients who learn to cope with chronic pain is that they appear more youthful, energetic, and joyous.)

The listeners sought Penney out to learn what she knew, so that they might overcome some of their own suffering. Penney met with them as a group in the church, which became two groups which became three groups. Out of this grew the American Chronic Pain Association, a self-help organization for those with chronic pain. There are now over 500 gorups in 49 states, 6 Canadian provinces, and even Australia and New Zealand. The number of groups continues to double about every one and a half years.

A casual consideration of the numbers of people who are in need of help coping with chronic pain can lead to a sense of futility. The need seems to be more than any health care system could satisfy. Yet if one person helps two people, who in turn help four people, and so on, assistance is quickly available to thousands. And the cost to society is that of a pot of coffee, an empty room in a church basement, and some newsletters.

Erik Erikson, often considered America's foremost psycho-analyst, described the human life cycle as a progression through a series of stages. He referred to adulthood as the stage of "generativity versus stagnation." By this he meant that the person who has been able to transcend self-absorption and per-sonal needs and to work for the betterment of his or her pro-geny, society, or world has attained an important aspect of mental health and maturity.

This concept of generativity is not only an apt description of Penney's progression from dealing with her own pain to helping others similarly afflicted, but equally describes the steps ACPA group members are urged to take, as they help direct others to more effective ways of coping.

The board of directors that Penney has recruited for the ACPA is a dedicated group of professionals from diverse fields. Their enormous commitment of time and work is a tribute to Penney and a confirmation that we can all derive meaning from investing ourselves in that which exceeds and outlasts us, and consists in the ongoing work of improving the human lot.

This book is about responsibility, which is unrelated to blame. Eventually, it is necessary to relinquish demands that others provide a solution they do not possess. Finally, one must cease reassuring oneself with "if only's" ("I could work, play, socialize if only.") One must let go of excuses ("If it weren't for pain, my boss, the kids, I would"). Accepting that the person with pain will determine the sort of life he or she has is both liberating and encumbering. It is empowering and burdensome. It compels attention to the question of what is left of life and how it will be spent.

This is a story of suffering and meaning. It addresses paradoxes: that acceptance of hopelessness can provide a pathway to new optimism; that working with the body helps one to transcend the body; that victory may begin with surrender. Finally, it is the story of a woman who was my patient but became my friend. She has provided me with the gift of evidence for my belief that the best guides are those who were once lost in the wilderness themselves, and were able to find their way out.

Edward C. Covington, M.D.
Cleveland, Ohio

CHAPTER 1

Life Before the Pain

Pain for most people has a beginning and an end. At first the pain makes them uncomfortable, but soon they start to notice an improvement and quickly are back to their usual selves. The unpleasant sensations are gone.

But imagine how it would be if there were no end to your headache or if your muscle soreness grew worse instead of better. Imagine a pain that has no end, that goes on day after day, draining you of all hope that it will ever come to an end. Imagine pain that will not allow you to get a decent night's sleep, to move about, to sit for any length of time, or even to enjoy the company of friends and family. It is a pain that cannot be driven out of your thoughts and from which you cannot be distracted. Consider what life must be like when every attempt to move makes you fearful that you will be unable to endure the pain. Such pain isolates you, puts a wall between you and your loved ones. That is the kind of pain I had to deal with for six years of my life.

This book is the story of that pain and how eventually, with a lot of help, I overcame it. It is not a heroic story. I am no heroine. But I am back to being a full person again. I hope that this account of my experiences will help others who have similar pain or who have loved ones with this sort of pain.

The Beginning

My life truly began when I met Scott, my husband. I could remember no other time in my life when I felt so important, so wanted, and so loved. It was Scott's love that seemed to pull me from the sense of worthlessness and being unloved, to someone who actually felt worthy of any kind of love at all. For the first time in my life I accepted who I was, not wishing to be anyone else. I was, in the truest sense of the word, happy.

I was married just after my twentieth birthday. I didn't really care how big or how fancy the wedding was. All I knew was that I loved Scott and I wanted to be married to him. I felt lucky to have had someone like Scott interested in me, and I suspect that I wanted to tie the knot before he changed his mind. I was somewhat uncertain in the early stages of our relationship. I found it difficult to understand why he was in love with me. I believed that marriage was forever, and once married, we would be as one.

We were very happy together. Right after our first anniversary, I gave birth to a little girl, Kimberly. Of course our life had its ups and downs over the next few years, but even when Scott was drafted, we stuck together and made the most of it. We worked well together and agreed on most major decisions. We celebrated our fourth anniversary in our first new home. Our lives seemed to blend well together, and we felt the time had come to have another child. We hoped for a boy, and in February of 1974 Scotty was born. I felt blessed.

The birth had been much easier than Kimberly's. My first meeting with my son, however, did not go well. As I stepped out of bed, eagerly waiting for the nurse to bring him in for his first feeding, I was stopped by an intense pain in my head the likes of which I had never experienced before. The only thought in my mind was relief of the pain. My son was all but forgotten.

Because of the type of person I was, never complaining about anything, especially pain, I did not say anything at first. I was afraid of something being terribly wrong, which would interfere with what I thought was a perfect storybook life. I did eventually, after a day of increasing pain, tell the nurse that I had a headache. Tylenol was ordered but did no good.

I remained silent about my pain, believing it would go away as soon as I returned home. It did not. I had little if any desire to care for either of my children, my home, or my husband. Eventually I called the doctor and was given a prescription for Valium, which did nothing for the pain.

I was not willing, or perhaps not strong enough, to deal with seeking relief of the pain. I was afraid of being seen as weak, out of control, or perhaps making too much out of nothing. Yet the pain did take control of me. If it had not been for my neighbor, Joanne, I don't know what I would have done. She willingly took care of Scotty and Kimberly while I remained in bed, unable to lift my head from the pillow.

As each day passed, I told myself it would go away, it had to. By the seventh day I was able to get out of bed and do a few simple chores around the house. Since I had just had a baby, there were few expectations of me. Everyone who called understood that I was "just tired." I told no one about the pain. I thought I was protecting myself.

Only sheer determination and building guilt kept me going. I had never allowed an illness to get me down, and I wasn't going to give in now. I think I was afraid Scott would love me less if I were not able to be the active, healthy person he had married. I had to behave in a manner I felt was expected of me. I continued cooking complete meals, I kept the house spotless, and I tried to spend time with Scott and the kids. But by the time Scotty was fifteen months old, the pain made that impossible. I kept telling myself that if the pain were of a physical origin I would not have been able to function as I had since Scotty's birth. But eventually I found it too hard to ignore the pain any longer. Though afraid of be-

ing thought of as a "typical housewife" with a headache, a
malingerer, I had to admit defeat.

For fifteen months, I had not mentioned the pain to
anyone but Joanne, and then only on rare occasions. I had
gone for my six-week check up with the doctor and never told
him that I was still having terrible headaches. Perhaps I thought
the pain would gradually disappear. Instead, it continued to
increase, and soon the pain began to control my life. It was
only after I became completely worn out that I reluctantly made
an appointment with a doctor of internal medicine.

The Doctor

I felt weak and defeated as Scott and I walked down the
darkened hallway. I approached the doctor's office with a mix-
ture of emotions: fear, embarrassment, and humiliation, but
little hope.

Other than checkups during my pregnancy, I had not been
to a doctor since I had a physical for my driver's permit at
the age of sixteen. After all, I had been the one my parents
saw as "healthy as a horse." Besides, I had always felt intimidated by and uncomfortable with doctors. The result was
that even though my life had been controlled by pain for the
past fifteen months, it was hard for me to admit to myself
that I was justified in being there. It was easier to think that
probably nothing was really wrong.

The doctor's examination did not take long. He did the
usually tests. The only thing that surprised me was his comment about my running a low-grade fever. After he completed
his examination he asked me to get dressed and join him in
his office.

Scott was already seated when I walked in. Without explanation, the doctor told me he would like to put me in the
hospital for further tests. I sensed his concern as he continued
to explain that until I was in the hospital, I was not to get

out of bed except to go to the bathroom. My anxiety built as he spoke aloud the orders that he was writing: complete skull X-rays, spinal taps, complete blood workup, and complete bed rest. He then told Scott to make arrangements to bring me to the hospital in three days.

I sat quietly listening to what the doctor was saying. Many questions floated through my mind, but the words never reached my mouth. I wanted to know why the doctor was ordering so many tests, why he seemed so concerned, and why I was not even allowed out of bed. Questions rapidly churned in my head. Screams raced through my desperate thoughts, but with each breath I took, I swallowed my words. I was afraid, plain and simple. For months I had myself convinced that my pain was, if not real, at least controllable. Now, at last, I had to face uncertainty. There very well may be something wrong with me, but I was too frightened to ask what.

As we left the building, its grim mood of age and decline seemed to fit my low spirits. I did not know what the doctor expected to find wrong with me, and I had not asked. I was frightened and more than willing to wait until Sunday to find out.

After three weeks of brain scans, skull X-rays, neurological testing, spinal taps, physical therapy twice a day, cervical traction, and a steady stream of doctors asking repetitious questions, I was discharged.

It wasn't until after I was released from the hospital that Scott told me they had suspected a brain aneurysm. The only change from the day I was admitted was the cervical collar I wore to take the pressure off my neck and alleviate some of the pain in my head and neck. I also had a handful of prescriptions and another doctor's appointment. There was no explanation for what had caused my pain and no reason why I was getting worse each week.

The pleasure of my homecoming was overshadowed by my negative attitude. The concern that my family expressed made me feel uneasy; they kept asking me questions for which I did not have any answers. I was the one, or so I believed, who was able to deal with any situation. I had never allowed anything to get me down. Now I was faced with pain and frustration, which ate away at me relentlessly. I tried, after several weeks of building up a small amount of muscle tone, to pick up where I had left off before entering the hospital. I struggled day in and day out to pretend I was feeling fine. I tried to prove to everyone that I could in fact deal with this pain. I was afraid of showing a weakness that would not be accepted, a weakness that would earn me rejection.

Visits to doctors soon became a regular part of my life. Another pill was always prescribed in an attempt to eliminate some of the pain. The pills made me weak. I lost twenty pounds within a year's time, which made me look anorectic. My physical health grew worse with each visit to the doctor, and I grew more and more depressed. I was sent to a number of specialists in the Pittsburgh area in the hope that one of them could help me. Each time as I sat anxiously listening to a doctor tell me there was little he could do for me, I grew more discouraged. The advice was either to try a new drug or more physical therapy. Most of the time all anyone could say to me was, "Learn to live with it." After two and a half years of doctor shopping, I stopped going to them altogether and promised myself that I would overcome the pain, all by myself.

But all my efforts in the following eighteen months to conquer the pain were futile. It controlled my every thought and move, and I no longer cared what happened to me. It didn't matter to me at that point whether I lived or died.

CHAPTER 2

The First Six Years

Almost six years after the birth of my son, my life was completely dominated by my pain, which now affected both arms and one leg in addition to my neck. I had become housebound. Often the pain ruled my every move. I tried not to show my suffering, but any movement of my hands, even the slightest motion of a finger, produced a sharp gripping pain that shot brutally up the entire arm.

In the years that had passed since my son was born, I had experienced many emotions, none of them positive. I was angry because I could not take care of my children. I was physically worn out from the pain and the many side effects caused by medications. I was emotionally drained from the countless uncertainties of dealing with medical professionals. They were always telling me that they could do nothing for me, that I should do as little as possible. I hated myself more each day for my own weakness and inability to deal with the pain effectively. My life had become mere existence.

I had once more reached a point that made it necessary to return to the doctors for help. The past eighteen months of trying to deal with the pain had failed. I felt as if I were imprisoned in the dungeon of my body, and there was no escape.

I was more discouraged than ever as I returned to the doctors. I was now unable even to open doors for myself. I had great difficulty just getting undressed for the examination. I was terrified that I would eventually lose total use of my arms and that no one would know why it had happened.

Once again I was admitted to the hospital for more tests. They decided to focus more on my muscles than my nervous system. I underwent a muscle biopsy and a nerve conduction test, and saw even more specialists. I had a poor reaction to the medication: the Valium they prescribed made me incoherent. I was now sure that there was nothing that could be done for me. One doctor suggested that I see a hypnotist who was supposed to be getting good results in helping people deal with phantom pain (a neurological pain that feels as though it's in a part of the body that has been amputated—thus the term *phantom*).

Is that what they thought I had? Pain that wasn't there! His suggestion did me more harm than good. He just reinforced my feeling that I was crazy. A crazy, hopeless person!

Fibrositis was the diagnosis given to me. Very little was known about fibrositis, what caused it, how to treat it, how long it would persist. I had not received an answer to any of these questions. In my mind I sensed that the doctor made up the diagnosis to appease me.

After two weeks in the hospital I returned home. This time I did not try to keep up appearances. I no longer cared what happened or what people thought of me. I was alive, breathing, eating when someone put food in front of me, but I felt dead—devoid of desire, free will, emotions other than pain and fear.

The entire house was now in a depressed state. The children had no sense of security. I often felt angry with myself at my inability to care for them. In my despair I told Scott to take the children and leave me. I did not want to inflict my pain on them. I could see what it was doing to them. I did not want to be responsible for destroying any more lives than I already had.

Because of my age, and the many side effects of the Prednisone that I was taking, my doctor cut down the dosage and put me on eight Bufferin a day to compensate. About a week after that I got labyrinthitis (an inflammation of the internal ear causing vertigo). The doctor immediately took me off the Bufferin and insisted I go to the Cleveland Clinic for help. I didn't have the strength to fight his suggestion. I hoped that if I went there and they told me the same thing I had been hearing all along, everyone would leave me alone. Against my better judgment I agreed to go to the Clinic, although I felt a little guilty for wasting more time and money. Thus in the Fall I headed for the Clinic and began the process that would change my life.

CHAPTER 3

The Cleveland Clinic:
Diary of Seven Weeks
in the Pain Unit

OCTOBER 21, SUNDAY

The day was clear. The blue sky was a beautiful backdrop for the vivid colors of the leaves. The earth was just beginning to slip into autumn. Orange, warm golden tones, soft browns, and rich reds could be seen amidst the trees that cover the surrounding mountains of Pennsylvania and on into the flat terrain of Ohio.

I stared out the window of the car and wondered how God could create such beauty in the world, yet allow so much pain and hurt. My gloomy thoughts focused on where the car was going and the futility of it all.

No one will ever be able to help me. I wonder, is death as bad, as horrible as one is led to believe? Could the white light that I have heard referred to so often by those who have been dead momentarily be the merging of the heart and mind? Could this merging be the soul that is transported into the vast unknown territory called heaven? Heaven, a place where there is no hurt, no pain, no worry. Would I be better off dead?

11

It would indeed be an end to my pain and an end to the pain I have created for Scott and the children. Why is God allowing me to live? Why do I have to suffer so? What in God's name did I do that brought me to this end? Am I being punished for negative feelings? Or perhaps the punishment is for just being me—insignificant, confused, dumb me. Why, why? Should I focus on trying to see the light, the merging of my heart and mind to travel into the vast unknown, or do I have to continue to suffer on this earth? What went wrong? Poor Scott, he believes I will be better.

My thoughts of distant places faded away like the picture on the television when you press the off button; the life acted out on the screen only a dim memory as I glanced over at Scott. His eyes remained focused on the road. His expression reflected the same hopeful, determined attitude that he had maintained over the past few weeks. He seemed positive that the Cleveland Clinic held the key to restoring me to the person I was before the pain.

Scott never allowed himself to accept the idea that there was no way to alleviate my pain. He was always ready to get another opinion and eager for me to try a different medication. He tried to make my life easier by taking on many of my responsibilities. Yet in a strange way his positive attitude made it hard for me to communicate my fears and self doubts, and made me hesitate to look further for help.

"Are you ready for your big day tomorrow?" Scott broke the silence that had existed since we'd left our home over an hour ago.

"No." My eyes were still straight ahead.

"Come on, I can't believe that you aren't a little bit excited."

"No."

"Wonder how the kids will make out? I guess it won't hurt Kim to miss two days of school. If you have to stay there, I can come home and get her back to school." Scott hesitated a moment, taking his eyes off the road to look at me. His eyes were filled with concern. "Penney, what's wrong?"

"Nothing." My voice was void of feeling. I could not tell him that I had been wishing I were dead, my death, being the only way I could see an end to both my pain and his. That is something he would never understand.

"We should be in Cleveland in about two hours. It's not a bad drive is it?" he asked. The response he anticipated was evident in his voice.

"No, it isn't." Silence descended again.

I could feel the warmth of his flesh as our skin made contact. I was thinking that his skin was as warm as his heart when he said, "You remember my cousin Deb?"

"Yeah."

"I asked her to meet us for dinner tonight. My mom gave me her phone number. I think it will help you to get out for a while tonight instead of sitting around the hotel worrying about tomorrow."

"Oh."

As the car continued toward our destination, my mind went back to thinking about the soft, warm, embracing white light of death, the merging of my heart and soul. To come to my final resting place. To, for the very first time in six years, be at peace with myself and my body. Death is final, but until it comes, my pain will continue to eat away at me, body and mind, until there will be nothing left worth fighting for. The only rest I will ever have will be in the end.

It had been three hours since we'd left Pittsburgh, when Scott pulled into the driveway of the Clinic Inn. He was glad to get there. "Here we are. Looks like a nice place. Just leave everything in the car until we check in." His expression was calm and confident. "This is going to do it; it is all downhill from here."

"Great." I followed Scott into the hotel.

From the outside the Clinic Inn, which was located across the street from the Cleveland Clinic, resembled any other hotel. We walked into the lobby, where I stood waiting, watching, and wondering as Scott checked us in. My eyes scanned the people, hoping to find something to hold on to, something to reassure myself, but I found nothing.

Once Scott had registered, I followed him and the bellhop up to our room. I fell a few steps behind Scott as he kept pace with the bellhop. Reaching our room, my eye caught sight of the number on the door, 1313! I thought, My God! This is a mistake! as I hesitantly entered the room.

I sat in the soft, velvety, gold chair by the window gazing out. I was once again in my world of dreams. The sudden knock on the door startled me. I forced myself to focus on the door, unable to stop my hopeless ruminating about the end I awaited but knew would come only after a great deal more pain.

Scott got up from his chair and opened the door to let his cousin Deb in. "Well, how are you? It's been a while."

They embraced, truly happy to see each other, while I remained in my chair, feeling very much like an outsider.

Deb, a few years younger than I, had received her nursing degree from a university near Pittsburgh. I remembered visiting her at school. I was on my way to see my older sister, who lived in the same small college town, and took a few minutes to see Deb while I was in the area. I had tried to bond with all of Scott's family.

Deb lived in an old, run-down dorm into which freshman were crammed. The tiny rooms were built for two, but four were sharing the same crowded space. That memory gave me a warm feeling for a fleeting second.

Now she seemed a stranger to me. It had been ten years since I had visited her. Although I had seen her a few times since, we had no real bond. I had all but forgotten what she looked like and found myself scrutinizing this person.

A little more than five feet high, her small frame supported more weight than it should; her bright blue eyes sparkled with zest. She seemed to have a secure sense of herself. Her smile seemed a natural part of her.

As Scott had planned, all three of us went to dinner in one of the restaurants in the city. Both Scott and Deb seemed to enjoy each other's company as they caught up on what the other had been doing over the past few years. I could not share in their enthusiasm. My mind would not allow me to think of anything other than what tomorrow would bring.

"So, who is your appointment with?" Deb asked as if she were trying to pull me into their conversation. Her eyes looked directly at me, waiting for an answer.

"I forget his name, he is a rheumatologist," I replied softly, a trace of fear in my voice.

"Do you know what it is they are looking for? Or is this just to confirm a diagnosis?" Deb still maintained the dance of life in her eyes. Her very being seemed to shout out with zest and warmth.

"To confirm," I replied, trying to end the conversation before it got too far.

Scott turned his head toward me and gave me a perplexed look before saying, "She is going to get some answers finally. They have been fooling around in Pittsburgh, no real answers, only possibilities. This is where we should have been a long time ago. But sometimes it takes a while for certain people to see the light. Right Penney?" His eyes turned toward me. I only glared back.

"Penney, I know you're going to get some answers at the Clinic. It's a good place. I have a few friends working there. It's amazing how many people are processed through the Clinic each day." Deb, still focusing her attention on my upcoming appointment asked, "What exactly did your doctor at home tell you?" Her curiosity was hard for me to bear.

"He wasn't sure. I'll wait and see what happens tomorrow," I said softly, lacking any emotion.

Learn to live with it, that is what he really said, if you want to know the truth. But my God, I cannot learn to live with total desperation and pain. No one can. No one should have to. Learn to live with it-so easy for them to say. Do they really know what that does to someone? Do they?

"She really doesn't believe they will help. But she'll change her tune when she's better." Scott's optimism still seemed relentless.

Deb placed her coffee cup back in the saucer and focused her attention in my direction saying, "Well, your doctor must have felt it was to your advantage to come here. They don't send you all this way unless they're sure you'll benefit in some way."

"Yeah," I replied.

So someone else could tell me to learn to live with it. So that I would not bother him any more with my problems. I didn't get better. Doctors don't like it when their patients don't get better.

"Well, don't worry if they decide to put you in the hospital for tests, which they probably will. I'll come every night to see you. I know how difficult it can be, out of town and in a strange hospital. Don't worry Scott, I'll be there for her." Deb's eyes gleamed in the soft candlelight of the restaurant as she spoke.

"Okay." I was almost afraid that she meant what she said.

But I thought I understood why she was being so kind. Scott was the oldest grandchild in their family and the most respected. He was the one all the others admired. He was the first one to graduate from high school. The first to go to college. The first to get married. I was his wife, and therefore many of those same feelings of respect and admiration were directed my way.

As we said our final good-bye to Deb, a very long two and a half hours later, I hoped I would never see her again.

OCTOBER 22, MONDAY

The buildings that made up the Clinic complex were intimidating just to look at. The panoramic view was awesome, a massive collection of steel and cement shaped into multiple buildings of no particular plan or design, the inside a maze of seemingly endless corridors. The halls were empty of any true colors; only shades of gray covered the walls and floors.

Our destination was the information desk, hidden somewhere in the confusion of the Clinic. Fifteen minutes passed before we managed to find it. After giving the receptionist the necessary information, she sent us up to the fifth floor of the East Clinic.

We reached the fifth floor of the East Clinic with no problems. This part of the Clinic seemed older. The walls were pale and covered with finger prints and smears. Faceless people filled every chair in the waiting area, so we stood. I was already tired from the long walks through the oversized Clinic, and I leaned against the wall.

"Penney Cowan. Is there a Penney Cowan here?" the nurse called out seeming to startle everybody as her voice carried clearly above the hushed conversations of the waiting people. My first impression of her reminded me of the stereotypical cross old nurse one sees in movies. Her uniform was stiffly starched and hung way below her knees.

"Here." Scott called out distinctly, slightly raising his hand so she would notice him. With hesitation in each step, I walked toward her.

"Want to follow me?" It was not really a question but a command.

I was put into a little room filled with the usual things one would expect to find in an examining room. The nurse told me to have a seat, but before I could do so, she disappeared.

The room reminded me of one of the rooms at the hospital I had worked at as an X-ray technician. That room now seemed like a lifetime ago. It was colorful, but I could see no color. It had enough light, but I saw only the dim outline of the fixtures in the room. It may have been warm in there, but I felt nothing but the spine-chilling fear of my plight. What difference would this make? Did it really matter to the people here if I got better? I was just another face in the crowd. Just as all those people I had x-rayed in the past. I was careful with them, tried to be gentle with them, but I didn't know who they were. I didn't really care if they would be able to go home that night and prepare dinner for their family. I didn't really care if they would be able to return to work that day. All I really cared about was getting the best X-ray I could. I had become calloused to the needs of my patients over time.

Is that what was going to happen to me now? Was the doctor going to look at me as another set of statistics or as a human being with not only physical pain, but a great deal of emotional pain. Was he going to be aware of how desperately I wanted to get back to living life again? Would he know how difficult it was for me to be in the role of a patient? Or would he see me as just one more person who had nothing better to do but waste time and money complaining about something that was no big deal? Could I express to him the fear that raged inside of me when I allowed myself to think of all that I had gone through with no success? Would he understand me, or take time to try and understand my needs?

One thought kept coming back to me as I sat quietly in the room: there was no way out of my situation. I was convinced that if the doctors at the Clinic came up with a new diagnosis, something other than fibrositis, it would be something like cancer of the bone, a deteriorating muscle disease, or something so terrible there would be no end to my pain! If perhaps they found nothing new, I would be forced to continue my life with pain, which dominated my every thought and move. I was already aware that nothing could be done for fibrositis except to "learn to live with it." The situation was hopeless.

Finally, thirty-five minutes later, the door swung open. The door banged against the wall and ricocheted half closed, immediately getting my attention. Standing in front of me was an old, overweight, and rather disheveled man. He was the doctor.

Upon completing his examination of me and asking me a number of questions, which had all been asked many times before by his peers, he said in a raspy tone, "It's fibrositis. You have pain in all the right trigger points. We find that a lot of the pain caused by fibrositis is due to anxiety and poor sleep patterns. There are several things I am going to do for you." He began writing as he spoke. "I want the usual blood work done just to be certain we are not overlooking anything. We give patients a test to see what their anxiety level is, the MMPI. And I want you to see Dr. Covington. He has just started a new program here at the Clinic to help people learn to live with their pain. Maybe he can help you. There is nothing I can do for you."

He wrote a few orders down on my chart, told me he would see me again in six weeks, and sent me back to the nurses station. He was finished with me.

What in God's name did I come all this way for? He couldn't care less about what happens to me. He is not being fair!

He had formed an opinion of me. He assumed I was just another malingerer, another housewife, and he didn't really know me. He didn't understand how desperately I wanted to get better. I was willing to go through hell and back if only the pain would stop.

In retrospect, I must give the doctor credit for an accurate diagnosis. I was fortunate that he did not try to satisfy my need for immediate answers or instant treatments, which would have only been harmful to me. It was my desperate need for relief from the pain that created such a negative reaction toward him. I had expected the Clinic to be different, unique in everything they did, from the questions they asked to the way they carried out an examination. I now realized that in spite of my apparent reluctance to come to the Clinic, I had really been hoping for some new and different magic formula.

As I walked back out into the waiting area and forced my body slowly down the hall, I convinced myself that they thought I was crazy; that is why they were giving me the test.

And the new doctor, he has to be a shrink! Why does everything have to be so hard? Why can't I make them understand that I am a person and have feelings?

I found myself standing next to Scott saying nothing. Once again we were told to go down to the main desk to set up an appointment with the new doctor and to have my blood test and X-rays done. They also said I could get my MMPI (Minnesota Multiphasic Personality Inventory) test down there. Scott took my hand as we headed for the elevator. His confidence in the Clinic was still intact.

Once off the elevator, I directed Scott to a vacant corner in the main hallway and quietly said, "They want me to see another doctor at the Clinic. And take some kind of test, some anxiety test." I tried to remain calm, in spite of the quiver in my voice, as I continued, "Scott, they think I'm crazy. I know it! That new doctor is a shrink, I know it. Why don't we just give up now. I don't want to go any further. Please!"

"Come on Penney! You've come this far, and I know we're just about to find the answer. I see no reason to give up now." There was a controlled excitement in his voice. He put his arms gently around my shoulders and said, "Don't worry. You can't stop now. I didn't marry a quitter. I know the answer is here, but we've got to go the entire way, and that means seeing this doctor tomorrow." He guided me down the hall toward the information center. "It won't be as bad as you think. We'll get these blood tests done, and then I'll take you out for a nice dinner. That will make you feel better," he said with certainty.

I resented his optimism, his certainty. Why was I not allowed to be weak and to give up? Why did I have to keep trying? Why couldn't I just quit? Scott did not realize what a tremendous strain his optimism was creating, and I did not have the courage or strength to tell him. He was all I had. Whether or not I agreed with his thinking, I clung to him as hard as I could. I hoped some of his strength and positive attitude would rub off on me.

OCTOBER 23, TUESDAY

I spent a sleepless night worrying about another confrontation with still another doctor. I lay in bed as light from the moon filtered in and created unsettling shadows on the wall. My mind tried to block out the coming day, but I had little success in ignoring my fears of what the next day would bring. I knew that I would once again have to go over my confusing medical history. All the suspicious looks, vague answers, and unsuccessful treatments of the past now haunted my thoughts. I was defensive every time I tried to describe the patterns of my pain. Now I would have to face my worst suspicions head on. I was going to see a shrink!

The next afternoon we went to the West Clinic where this Dr. Covington was waiting to pronounce still one more verdict on me. The West Clinic was a new addition. I felt uneasy as soon as we walked in. Not a chair in the lobby was empty. I thought that as we walked by, several people paused in midsentence, their expressions blank, and the newspapers, hiding faces, were bent at the corners as eyes followed us. An old couple, sitting against the window, stopped talking, and out of the corner of my eye I thought I saw him pointing directly at me. I could hear in my mind what they must be saying, "There goes another crazy person. Look at her! She's nuts. Poor woman, she's sick." I could almost feel their stares, hear their words. I was certain the entire West Clinic was set aside for psychiatric care. I held on to Scott even more tightly than before. Each step was more painful than the last, and with each step I took, my heart sank a little more.

Time all but stood still as we sat in the waiting room of the sixth floor of the West Clinic. I drew mental pictures of what this new doctor must look like. I expected him to resemble John Carradine, tall, lanky, and mysterious. He would speak in a low, almost hollow tone, never making eye contact, but looking right through me. His eyes would be penetrating. He would be able to read my every thought. He would twist each word I said to fit his way of thinking and what he wanted to believe.

I watched people going in and out of the room. I held my breath as each new doctor appeared at the door to call out a name. Each time I hoped that this one was not Dr. Covington. Suddenly I heard my name being called by a man I had not even noticed walk in.

He was not what I had imagined. He was young and short—about five seven—his blond hair cut in a style that left the front hanging down over his forehead, giving him a boyish look. His expression was gentle, not the usual stern "I'm too busy" look I had seen in other doctors.

I got up and walked toward him as he reached out his hand, and in a tone as gentle as his appearance said, "Hi, I'm Ed Covington. Want to come with me?"

Ed. Why "Ed" and not "Doctor"? Maybe he is not the right one. Maybe they made a mistake.

The hallway seemed endless. I could not keep up with him and fell several steps behind. We were almost at the end of the hall when he entered one of the offices. He motioned for me to have a seat. The chair directly beside his desk felt good as I sank down into the soft leather, but the chrome arms gave me a chill. I rested my head on the high back. My craving for a cigarette surfaced as he lit one, the smoke permeating the air. I had not smoked in three years, but I would have gladly had one at that moment.

Dr. Covington had such a relaxed manner about him. He seemed so comfortable in what I saw as a very threatening situation. He settled back in his desk chair. His weight shifted as he crossed his legs. In a soothing tone he asked, "Want to tell me something about yourself? What brought you to the Clinic?"

I was so scared I wasn't sure whether words would come out when I opened my mouth. I tried to think of a way to present myself without sounding like a hypochondriac. With a great deal of hesitation in my voice I began, "Well, my doctor, the one in Pittsburgh, sent me here. He said I had fibrositis, and he had done all he could. Yesterday I saw a rheumatologist who confirmed what he said, and here I am. I have had trouble for six years. I just want to be able to take care of myself and my family.''

"What kind of tests have you had?'' he asked as he reached for his coffee, taking a sip as his eyes remained on me.

"A lot.''

He glanced down at my file lying in front of him for a moment before he said, "I can see you have. There is no need to go into all that again.'' His tone was somehow comforting to me as he asked, "What about you? How do you feel about all this?''

"I want to get better. I have to get better.'' My voice still trembled.

He took a final puff on his cigarette, smashing it out in a small tin ashtray sitting on the corner of his desk as he said, "What I want to do is get some basic information about you, as a person. You're married. Right?''

"Yes.''

"How many children?'' He began writing, his eyes now directed away from me, yet he still communicated a sense of gentleness by his voice.

"Two.''

"Their ages?''

"Six and eleven.''

"Are your mother and father still living?''

"Yes.''

"How do you feel about them? Do you get along with them?'' He stopped writing as he spoke directly to me. He waited for an answer.

I replied, "They're my parents. I guess the same way anyone else feels about their parents.'' I could see by the "what do you mean" expression on his face that he needed more explanation. "I never gave them any trouble. I always helped around the house. I have always been willing to do whatever

I could for them. They never really seemed to care what I did. They have been good to me.''

Without any indication of how he felt about my answer, he asked, ''How much schooling did you have?''

I was intimidated by his question. I explained, ''High school and two years of X-ray training.''

''What kind of grades did you get?''

I knew the answer I was about to give would not relay my commitment to prove myself determined and in control. ''Well, in high school they weren't so good. I couldn't get into college. But for some reason I made the dean's list every time in training.''

''Do you know why that is?'' His gaze remained on me. He still had given no reaction to anything I had said.

''No.'' Thinking a moment, I said, ''I guess it was easier.''

''What did your parents say about the kind of grades you had in high school? Did they try to help you at all?'' he asked curiously.

''They were too busy. They really didn't seem to care if I brought home A's or D's.'' Regret filled my voice.

''Are you close to your parents?''

''I was before the pain. Now.''

''Now, what?''

''I don't know. They are both very busy.''

''Too busy for you?''

''I don't think so. Just busy.''

''Could you talk with your parents? Tell them what was going on in your life?''

''Not really. They really didn't seem to care what I did. I always did exactly what they told me.'' I was only half aware of what I was saying. No one had ever asked me these types of questions before, and I had never really given much thought to my relationship with my parents.

''Were you happy as a child?''

''No.'' I replied. I was so nervous that my answers flew from my mouth before I realized what I was saying.

"Why is that?"

"I don't know. I guess I always felt . . . not good enough . . . a disappointment to everyone. I was overweight, very overweight until I was about eighteen."

"Were your parents upset by your weight problem?"

"No. They really didn't seem to care one way or another."

Without any further questions about my childhood, he asked, "How are things with you and your husband?" His tone was now more professional, not quite so soft.

"We don't have any problems, except the pain."

"How is your sex life?" he asked, still maintaining his professional demeanor.

"Okay." I answered, extremely uncomfortable with the question.

"I don't believe that!" He sat up in his chair, a smile on his face, his tone livelier. "Sex is either great or bad, but not okay." He chuckled to himself and asked, "What is it? Bad or great?"

I hesitated to answer. I didn't think it was any of his business, and to avoid getting into any kind of long discussion, I said, "Great."

"We'll talk about that later. What else can you tell me about yourself? What do you enjoy doing?" Once again, gentleness in his voice.

"I don't know. There isn't much to tell. I like to cook, take care of my home and family. What do you want to know?"

A silence fell over the room as he turned his head and stared out the window. Each second felt like minutes as I waited anxiously for him to say something, anything.

He held the pen that had been resting on his desk and then quickly glided across the paper before he stopped and said. "I have picked up several things from the few things you said. The first is that you don't really like yourself too much. You have felt inadequate all your life. And the second is that you feel your parents didn't care about you."

My heart began pounding in my chest as he spoke. I hadn't said that, or at least I didn't remember saying those things. But . . . it was true! Those were my hidden feelings.

"From what you've told me and what I can see of you and your willingness to talk, I think there is a good chance I can help you.

My God, he'll help me!

"It's going to take a lot of effort on your part. Let's bring your husband in here, and I'll explain the program to both of you." He reached for the phone and asked to have Scott sent in.

I tried to be cautious. I did not want to allow myself to get set up for another disappointment. I had to be careful not to build up my hope only to have it shattered again. If there was one thing I had learned in the past six years, it was not to be too optimistic too soon. No matter how hard I tried, no matter how sincere the doctor had been in his efforts to help me, it had never, ever worked out. The pain always remained. Yet I could not ignore the fact that he said there was a good chance he could help me. It was the first time in six years of pain that anyone had ever said there was hope.

Scott joined us. Dr. Covington directed his attention toward Scott as he explained, "I have talked to your wife. I feel that there are several areas that she really has to work on; I can go into detail later. She seemed willing to talk to me."

I caught a glimpse of Scott's eyes. They were filled with excitement and anticipation at what Dr. Covington was saying. He looked so relaxed and all together sitting there.

"What we can offer her is, I think, a way for her to get back to having fun instead of this pain. We have a pain unit designed to help people just like her, those who have tried just about every conceivable form of medical treatment possible without success." He paused a moment and turned his attention to me. He looked directly at me. His voice was so calm, so kindhearted as he continued, "It's time for her to stop looking to medicine to make her better and do it for herself. We can teach her how to do that through our program. It will now be up to her to be responsible for her own physical therapy. No more passive therapy for her. She will have to act like a person while she is here. The entire staff is trained to ignore all kinds of sick behavior. Only positive behavior will be rewarded. Things like biofeedback, exercise, group therapy will take up most of her day."

He paused for a moment as he searched through his desk drawer for a paper. "Here, this pretty much tells you all you'll need to know about the program. Like I said, she seems willing to talk and is rather open about her feelings. Usually it takes from three to eight weeks for our people to complete the program. I feel pretty sure she'll be able to leave in about three weeks, barring any problems.

"You know I'm a shrink?" he then asked very nonchalantly. "Well, I have been given five beds to work with here at the Clinic. The only problem you might have is that they are all on the psych ward." He spoke directly to me. "Do you have any reservations about staying there?"

What could I say? He told me he could help me to overcome my pain. All I would have to do is agree to enter the crazy ward. I just looked at him, then I looked at Scott, hoping he would say something, anything. Nothing! The decision would have to be mine. What it came down to was how desperate was I. Was I desperate enough to allow this to happen to me, straitlaced Penney?

Yes! There was no other choice. I had crossed all the other bridges available to me and had gotten nowhere. I was still young and I had too many things in my life left to do. Yes, I was desperate enough to agree to be admitted to the psych ward.

Very softly I said, "I guess I can handle that," although I felt quite uncertain in my heart.

"When do you think you will be ready to come?" He now sounded too eager to get me on his unit, which gave me an uncomfortable feeling.

I needed time and space to get ready. The kids would have to be taken care of. That was my first concern. Things had to be put in order at home before I would be able to leave for such a long period of time. We made arrangements to call Dr. Covington at the beginning of the week. That would give me time to prepare myself.

As we left the Clinic that afternoon, Scott was on cloud nine. He was excited about the prospect of my returning to my old healthy self. He had no idea how difficult the road ahead would be for me. He didn't consider the circumstances I would have to deal with on the psych ward. I could only imagine what it would be like, but I was sure that no matter how terrible I thought it might be, the reality would be ten times worse.

As we walked out of the Clinic that day many thoughts ran through my mind. In all the confusion and uncertainty, only one thing remained clear; there was hope. We finally had something to hang on to.

OCTOBER 24-30, WEDNESDAY

Time went by faster than I expected. I managed to get everything into order without too much difficulty. We found someone who would stay with the children while I was away. I called a few of my best friends, and I told even them only what I wanted them to know. I asked them to relay the message to others. I could not face anyone. I even had trouble talking with Scott. I kept all my feelings locked tightly inside and shared my fears with no one. The pain in my body intensified with each passing day. I had not taken any medication at all since the week before my appointment at the Clinic, and I blamed my increased pain on that. It took me five times as long to do something as simple as folding cloth.

By the end of the week I felt that I had little to say to anyone, and no one said very much to me. Even Scott became more subdued. His "I know you're going to make it" statements stopped after the third or fourth day we were home. No matter what he said to me, I found a way to twist his words and cut off any chance of relaxed conversation. I wanted to be left alone. Scott and I grew further apart each day. I could handle the distance more easily than his sincere love and concern for me. No longer would I allow him to embrace me, kiss me, or do anything that would spark tenderness between us. I was closing the door on my own emotions by shutting off any communication before it started. I would actually walk away from Scott as he spoke. I refused to help Kim with her homework. Scotty's attempts to get my attention, telling me jokes or doing the silly things that in the past I would laugh at, failed as I shut him mentally out of my life as if he did not exist. Distancing myself from my family emotionally was one of my ways of coping with my fear of never returning home at all, or of never being the person they wanted me to be. If I didn't care for them, then it would not hurt me so much if I failed. I also thought, during those last few days at home, that distancing myself from them would help them in the end to adjust to never having me home again. Dr. Covington's promise of help, which had sparked some small hope, I now did not believe. I was certain I would fail.

OCTOBER 28, SUNDAY

Sunday night, after the kids were tucked away, Scott and I sat down to watch television. No words were spoken, only an occasional laugh or snicker from Scott, as we watched *One Flew Over the Cuckoo's Nest*. Jack Nicholson portrayed a patient in what I assumed was a factual account of life on a psychiatric ward. I sat there soaking in every gesture, feeling each situation as if I had been in the room with them. My mind kept seeing parallels between the ward in the film and what the ward at the Clinic would look like. I visualized one massive room filled with people, strange, grotesque-looking people. Their eyes would be sunken, hollow, and lifeless. Their hair dirty and uncombed making them look uncivilized. They would all have the same wrinkled scrub suits on, yellowing and dirty, food stains running down the front of them as they dribbled food, unable even to feed themselves. Their clothes would be hanging, all buttons and ties removed for safety. Definitely, the ward would be staffed by huge, overbearing men who would stand in each corner of the room. They would watch and wait, hoping for a patient to get out of line. Then they would use brute force to restrain the out-of-control patients as they carried them off to a tub filled with steaming hot water. They would force them to remain in the steam bath for hours as punishment. I fantasized that a nurse, much like Nurse Ratchett in the movie, would be waiting for me at the Clinic. She would be sly, controlling, manipulative, and sneaky, always forcing people to anger. She would never show compassion, arousing only fear in her patients.

While we watched the movie, I was conjuring up terrible thoughts of the psychiatric ward at the Clinic, but Scott was enjoying it, laughing at those people who were so out of control they were unaware of their actions. They made fools of themselves as they acted more like children than adults. I resented Scott more and more with each burst of laughter. I convinced myself that he was reflecting many of the same feelings he had about the movie toward me also.

Watching that movie was a big mistake. It made the next few days insufferable. Thoughts of being put in a similar situation where I would not be able to think for myself or to be free, haunted me.

OCTOBER 29, MONDAY

Monday morning I called Dr. Covington to let him know I was ready. We agreed on Wednesday morning as the admission date. Everything was set. There was nothing more to be said.

OCTOBER 30, TUESDAY

Scott turned into the narrow driveway of Deb's house. A limb from an old, gnarled maple hung low over the driveway, scraping my window. My heart began pounding in my chest. Although the light at the front of the house gave off a warm glow as if to say welcome, I felt reluctant to get out of the car.

It had been Scott's idea to spend the night at Deb's. He felt it would be easier on me to stay there than face another night in a strange hotel. What he hadn't considered was the difficulty that faced me in telling Deb all the details of my stay at the Clinic.

A small part of me was angry at Scott for placing me in this situation in the first place. I did not tell my own parents where I was going to be. How could I tell a distant relative that I was about to be placed in a unit that would (or so I believed at the time) take away my freedom of speech and action? I thought to myself, "Scott should be the one to break the news to Deb."

"I have to tell you something." I struggled to find the right words that would ease the blow. Words that would make my stay at the Clinic seem less horrible than I knew it would be. I had to tell her. I could not let her come to see me and then find out where I was without really understanding. I knew I could not handle her rejection.

I stood against the counter in her kitchen as she poured coffee. "Have you ever heard of Dr. Covington?" I hoped that she hadn't found out on her own.

"I asked a few nurse friends of mine who work at the Clinic, but they have never heard of him. I guess that's because he is new," she said matter-of-factly, as she continued to fill the three mugs with coffee.

Trying mentally to prepare myself for the reaction I pre-
sumed she would have—total rejection—I continued. My eyes
were fixed on the floor. "Well, he is the head of the pain
unit." I shifted from one foot to the other as I continued.
"He is a . . . a . . ." I had to tell her; I had to cross my first
obstacle. I could feel the sweat beading on my brow as I continued, "a psychiatrist."

"I figured he might be." Her tone had not changed. My
eyes made contact with hers as she spoke.

How did she know that? She isn't upset!

"Oh, Penney, don't worry about it. The Clinic is a famous
place. You will be in good company. You might even see
Elizabeth Taylor on the ward." Her voice was filled with
understanding. She was so unaffected by my statement!

I waited nervously for a delayed reaction, for my words
to be processed in her mind. There was none. As far as Deb
was concerned, there was nothing wrong with what I was about
to do. She hardly knew me and yet she was willing to give
me the benefit of the doubt. She was still willing to visit me
every night, still willing to accept me for myself and not for
what I was going to be doing.

I followed her back into the living room. As I sat down
on the couch, my body welcoming the support, she handed
me my coffee. She did not see Scott quickly take the mug out
of my hands, the weight of it making it difficult for me to
hold, as she walked across the room to the chair in the far corner of the room, her calm voice saying, "It will be hard, I
know that. But this doctor has got to be good or he wouldn't
be practicing at the Clinic." Her expression was sincere and
she looked right at me as she spoke. Her words reassured me—a
little.

I was still very apprehensive about the next day, but Deb
had managed to make me feel less like a freak. She had some
understanding of what I felt. We had quickly established a

rapport that would allow me in the coming weeks to look to Deb for moral support. She was there for me through the entire ordeal.

OCTOBER 31, WEDNESDAY

It was the end of October, but along the edge of the driveway leading up to the main Clinic the marigolds and geraniums were still blooming as if it were July. For a moment their beauty almost made me forget why I was there.

Shortly after arriving, I found myself sitting silently in the lobby of the South Clinic. This building appeared to be as new and modern as the West Clinic. I watched people pass by and wondered if they knew why I was there. I always worried about what people might be thinking of me. I decided that the young couple sitting in silence across from us, their hands entwined, were headed for the psych ward also. I felt very conspicuous, as though my destination was apparent to everyone in the waiting area. I took only a few minutes out to go back to a small office and fill out the necessary papers before returning to the waiting room to watch and be watched.

"Penney Cowan?" I saw a tall, slender woman dressed in a dark suit calling my name. Her words cut through the quiet like an arrow rushing through the stillness of the deep woods, swish and hitting its mark with a disturbing thump.

"Here." I stood up slowly. "Hi, my name is Stella. I am a nurse and I work with Dr. Covington on the pain unit. I'm so glad they had you come in early. It is not often we get a chance to get all the paper work done on a new patient before lunch. Follow me, I'll take you up," she said hurriedly as she looked at me. I felt as if she were looking right through me.

"Is this your husband?" Stella asked.

"Scott Cowan, nice to meet you." Scott stood up and reached out to shake Stella's hand. Stella appeared to be in her early fifties, though her glasses with their tinted lenses might have added a few years. Her manner conveyed a firm sense of inner strength and self-confidence. Although her voice had an unpleasant harshness, the rhythm of her conversation never broke for a moment. She was completely matter-of-fact and businesslike, her manner conveying little in the way of sympathy or compassion. I took an instant dislike to her. She reminded me of Nurse Rachett in *Cuckoo's Nest*—very controlling!

Our excursion through the halls of the Clinic lasted about fifteen minutes and ended at the West Clinic on the seventh floor, just above where I had met Dr. Covington a little over a week before. My leg was aching; the couch in the alcove directly across from the elevator was tempting, my body crying out for rest, as we stepped out of the elevator.

The alcove was drab and cold, and there was a heavy feeling in the air I could not explain. Then, as we turned the corner I saw it: a large brown door with a heavy glass panel reinforced with wire mesh! A door that had to be opened with a key!

"We keep this door locked all the time because of some of the psych patients on the floor. I'll show you how to get in and out later. Right now I'll show you where your room is," Stella said, not effected in the least by the presence of the door—the door to my cage. She pulled a small ring of keys out and opened the door with ease. She stood to one side, propping it open with the toe of her shoe to allow me to enter.

"Come into my parlor," said the spider to the fly

I hesitated to step inside. I knew that once I did so I would be at their mercy. Scott took my hand and gently led me in. The ward was different from what I had imagined. The ward in *Cuckoo's Nest*, while it was all one open area, was well lit, one entire wall comprised of windows. This ward was dull and lifeless, its only window at the far end of the hall. Its drab, light green walls and carpet appeared to have been badly abused. But it did afford some privacy. Individual rooms lined both sides of the long hall. We walked almost to the other end of it before coming to a stop. The numbers 7-B-28 were etched into a thick black piece of plastic affixed tightly to the door. This was to be my room.

My first impression of the room was negative. Though large, it was somehow very oppressive. My eyes went immediately to the window. I expected to see bars. Instead the windows were covered with plexiglass.

The wall to my left accommodated two hospital beds, the only sign that it was a hospital room at all. I would not have been surprised to see restraining straps hanging from the frame of the beds, but there were none. Although the wall was painted bright orange, it managed to look gloomy and dismal. To my right, directly opposite the orange wall and spanning the length of the room was a long piece of furniture, in relatively good condition. It contained two desks, a series of drawers, and a cupboard, all in blond wood. Opposite the doorway, the window went from one end of the wall to the other. In front of it was a square table and two orange-and-brown plaid soft-cushioned chairs, threadbare in the front. The room was intended to be attractive and comfortable, but I saw it as my prison for an indefinite period of time. Time, that was all I had now—empty time.

I was brought back to the here and now by Stella's voice. "This used to be the Clinic Motel, but when we had a real problem with bed space, they decided to convert these rooms into patients' rooms. I'll tell you one thing, these beds are very hard to get. You are lucky you got one. We have a lot of people waiting to get in here." Stella's voice softened somewhat as she patted the bed and went on her way. Scott and I stood looking at each other, speechless. I saw before me for the first time someone who did not appear completely confident. He stood still, his hands in his pockets. His eyes slowly scanned the room, avoiding any eye contact with me. He was visibly uneasy. His lack of certainty was evident by the blank expression on his face.

I had used a great deal of energy to make it that far. My body ached, my arms were so sore I had to sit down and rest them on my lap in a vain attempt to take some of the strain off them. My head was pounding as I tried to focus on the good that would come out of this, but I could not get the images of *Cuckoo's Nest* out of my mind. I looked at Scott and saw an empty person with nothing to say. He appeared to be feeling as trapped as I was. Entering the room had brought us down to reality.

The rest of that morning, matters got worse. Two orderlies went through all of my personal belongings. They counted each article, removing anything they thought might pose a threat to me or the other patients. They did not miss a thing. They left me fearing that I might not be safe there and feeling humiliated.

Stunned by the lack of sensitivity thus far, I literally collapsed into the chair hoping this day would come to an end then and there. I knew I did not have the strength to withstand much more. My anticipation of what this place would be like had not been unrealistic; 7-B was unfeeling, cold, and demoralizing. At that moment I would have gladly agreed to bear my pain indefinitely just to escape this horrible place.

But instead of escaping, I found myself answering Stella's questions, all of which I had answered many times before. She ended her questions with, "There are several things that you have to be made aware of—rules we have. You are not allowed to bring any drugs or alcohol on the ward. If you do, you will be asked to leave, and you will not be permitted to reenter at a later date. If you go out on pass, you'd best be back by the specified time. If you fail to return for the night, you will automatically be discharged from the hospital and will have to be readmitted at a later date. The insurance companies are very adamant about that." Stella's words ran through my mind as I tried to make some sense of them. Her tone was one of distrust. Each statement made me feel more like a criminal than a patient, as if she were expecting me to disobey her commands.

"Scott, you are going to have to see Dr. Powers, a psychologist who works with our patients' families, before you leave. She fills the family members in on their role in the program. I have you down for a one-thirty appointment," Stella said as she gathered up all her papers. She was done with me.

The most persistent thought going through my mind was knowing I would fail. I realized, as I sat in the isolation of that lifeless room, that I had only agreed to come here so that Scott would finally realize that there was no hope for me. If I did spend the time in what he considered to be the answer to our prayers and remained in the same painful state, then perhaps he would realize that there was nothing more to be done for me. He would then have to let me go. He would have to admit defeat. This was the last stop for me on a very long, frustrating journey. Yes, at that moment I knew I would fail. Any shred of hope I might have had when I first talked with Dr. Covington was now gone. I unconsciously replaced hope with a stubborn determination to fail.

I really was alone now. Scott had been taken away from me to see Dr. Powers. The morning's stress had intensified my pain. I was content just to sit alone, motionless and quiet in my room and hope that no one would come in to make any request of me. My eyes remained fixed in a blank stare, and I didn't even notice the woman who had walked into my room until she was standing directly in front of me, her voice startling me.

"Well, who are you? My name is Suzy. You must be my new roommate." Her tone was filled with delight as she introduced herself.

"Yeah, my name is Penney." While she seemed pleased to have someone to talk with, I resented her intrusion.

"I've been here two days already. Most of the time getting a bunch of tests done. I'm glad to finally have a roommate. It gets mighty quiet here at night." I detected a southern accent in Suzy's voice as she continued "You just wait. They are going to keep you so busy you ain't gonna have time to turn around. But I keep gett'n these tests, see, and they still ain't sure what's wrong with me.'' Suzy paused to bend down and pull her pant leg up, ''See this knee! It wasn't like that a few days ago. Just sort of puffed up overnight, imagine that.'' A note of amazement in her voice. Then she said, ''What's wrong with you? Why you're so young and pretty I can't imagine you hav'n any trouble.''

''Fibrositis,'' I replied, unwilling to go into any detail.

''Oh,'' she replied in a curious tone, like people do when they don't have the vaguest idea what you are talking about, but don't really care to know either. Suzy was in her mid-fifties; the many lines in her face immediately gave her age away. Although she was plain and, without any outstanding features, her personality and appearance were childish. Her hair, more gray than brown, clung tightly to her scalp in small ringlets in a hairdo I would come to hate.

I looked at her, wishing she would simply disappear from my sight, as she said, ''Sam he's my husband—he's stayin' with some friends here in Cleveland. He's gonna get me some new clothes. Dr. Covington says I'll be here for three weeks. Didn't expect that. Did you?'' She turned toward me but did not give me time to answer as she went on in her slow drawl.

''Penney and Suzy, you are supposed to be in creative therapy. Why are you still here?'' Stella asked as she walked into our room.

I had no idea what or where I was supposed to be. I was waiting for Scott to return and let me know how things went at his end. I didn't want to leave my room because he would not be able to find me, but Stella didn't leave me any choice.

Creative therapy was meant to relax the patients and keep them busy. I found myself sitting at a long table in the middle of a rather small room. The room was cluttered with paper, yarn, glue, and other items. The women working in this room treated the others around me as if they were small children. I resented being there, but I said nothing. I was so afraid to step out of line that I just did what I was told.

Finally Scott poked his head in the door of the creative therapy room, his blond hair catching my eye. "Penney, I've got to run. The kids will be waiting for me to take them out trick-or-treating. I'll call you tonight," he said hurriedly as he turned away and disappeared.

"Well, how is everything so far? You making out okay?" Dr. Covington asked nonchalantly as he sat himself down on one of the chairs in my room. "Have you met most of the staff?"

"No." Fear was apparent in my voice.

"Well, you will soon enough. Your blood tests are in from last week. As I expected, there was nothing we didn't already know. I want to start you on a drug." He stopped to light a cigarette. This time I joined him. I had asked Scott to pick up a carton of cigarettes for me before we came to Cleveland. I felt they might help me to cope better with this place. As the smoke circled in an upward motion toward the ceiling, he began to explain in a more professional tone now, "We are going to try you on 75 milligrams of Elavil. It has been very effective in treating fibrositis. We'll see how you do on that and take it from there."

"Okay." Hurt was in my voice as I spoke. I knew that Elavil was an antidepressant. I was now more certain than ever that I was on 7-B because I was mentally, not physically, sick.

"You will be meeting several people today." He stopped a moment to look at my chart, which lay on his lap "Yeah, PT should do an evaluation on you. I'm going to have someone from pain therapy take a look at you also. Do you have any questions?"

"No." I was far too frightened to know what to ask.

Snapping the lid on his pen closed, he stood up. He turned toward me and said, once again more like the person I had met that first time instead of the doctor he was today, "See ya tomorrow. Keep your chin up, you are going to make it!"

Why my arms? Why did it have to be my arms? Why not
my legs? I could have lived with that. I could have dealt with
that, but my arms! I sat in my room, staring at my arms. I
was trying to find some reason for the pain, some explanation. Without my arms I was useless, I could barely take care
of myself. Watching television was about the only thing left
to fill the long hours with. My arms hurt *so much*! I tried to
remain calm and hide the deep aching pain that seemed to
worsen with each move I made. I wanted to cry, but as always,
I remained in control.

Was I being punished for something I had done at some
point in my life? Was God giving me just punishment for
something so terrible that I would be reduced to no more than
a painful, agonizing existence for the rest of my life? I often
tried to think back to a time in my life when I had been so
bad, mean, or unjust to someone or had done something so
unforgivable that it would justify what I was going through.
I never found an acceptable reason for being in so much pain.
It seemed so unfair that I should have to bear such pain when
there were others out there who were far more sinful than I.
Is this the cross I must bear? I would often ask myself, *why me?*

"Hello?" A quiet voice came from the doorway. As I
looked up I saw a man standing there, dressed in white from
head to toe "Is it okay if I come in for a minute?" He walked
toward me and sat down in the same chair Dr. Covington had
been in earlier.

"My name is Dr. Gabis. I have been assigned to you while
you are on 7-B." He spoke with a mellow but assertive accent. "I will talk with you each day, spend a lot of time with
you getting to know you better. I hope to be able to help you
any way I can. Right now, however, I have to ask you some
questions. I know they might seem strange, but nevertheless,
here goes."

Why can't they just leave me alone? What are they going to
accomplish by asking more questions? This was a mistake coming here, a big mistake-there is no hope for me.

"How do you sleep?"

"Not well." Even though he was soft spoken, I was still intimidated by him and my voice shook.

"Do you ever hear voices, inside your head?" His eyes were directly on me as he spoke.

I wrinkled my brow as I said, "No."

With no change in his tone he asked, "Do you ever feel like someone is watching you?"

"No!" Irritated by the question.

"Can you count for me by seven backwards from one hundred?"

What in the world will that get me? They think I'm crazy! I think they might be right.

"One hundred, ninety-three, eighty-six, seventy-nine."

"Okay. That's far enough," he said, stopping me from counting.

In spite of his ridiculous question, he had a tone of compassion in his soft voice. His lips were full. His jaw angled slightly to the left as he spoke. But when he told me that he would have to give me another physical, it immediately threw my mind into a spin. Hadn't I been through enough already? Didn't they get all there was? Being reexamined seemed repetitious, but I didn't say a word. I played the passive role of a good patient despite what Dr. Covington had said—that I would not play that role there.

Upon completing his examination, Dr. Gabis said, "I would like to have a neurologist look at you. I found something questionable, and I want to have it checked out. I'm sure it's nothing Dr. Covington is not already aware of. For the most part, you seem to be in good health." He put his stethoscope around his neck, each end hanging down on his chest, moving up and down with each breath.

The doubt began to take over my mind again. Had they missed something? Was there an undiscovered reason for my pain? Was there something they could do besides putting me on the psych ward where it was so difficult to cope and where I felt incarcerated? Was my being there a mistake? My mind was like a cyclone, swirling questions around in my head. I so desperately wanted the entire experience on 7-B to be a mistake that I grasped eagerly at what Dr. Gabis said. I hoped that they had missed something, that my being there was a mistake. I let no one know how I felt, but I knew deep down inside that the doubt I had picked up from Dr. Gabis would interfere with my effort to participate 100 percent in the program. If something had been overlooked, I might make matters worse by following through with the exercise program. Not until I got the word from the neurologist would I be convinced beyond a shadow of a doubt that 7-B was my only hope.

OCTOBER 31, WEDNESDAY EVENING

The sun was slowly disappearing below the horizon. I stood by the window in my room watching the fiery ball fade into the skyline of Cleveland. Cleveland's flatness was much different from Pittsburgh's rolling hills. Here I could see for unrestricted miles. As the sun set, the city seemed like a make-believe village set on a platform, with only a few lights glittering in the distance beyond it. I stood looking out the window, wondering, hoping that soon I would be out there among other people, unnoticed and free.

The day had hit me hard. For the first time in my life, my freedom had been taken away. I was hidden from the rest of the world, but no matter how hard I tried in the coming weeks, there would be no place that I could hide from myself. I felt that 7-B had stolen my identity that day, but standing there, gazing out of my window, I had to wonder if I had ever had an identity of my own to begin with. Had I just been living in the shadows of others?

"Penney?" an uncertain voice called from the doorway of my room, breaking into my reflections. "This is a *big* place,"

Deb said as she entered my room, her nylon jacket rustling as she walked toward me. "I pulled the old 'I know where I'm going, I belong here' routine so I wouldn't have to stop and register downstairs at the main desk." Deb slipped off her jacket as she neared the window. "So, how is it going?"

I sat down in one of the chairs, looking at Deb, and without really answering her question, said with a note of surprise in my voice, "You came!"

"Of course I came. I told you I would," she replied, a little hurt that I had doubted her intentions. "I must admit I wouldn't pick this as a place to hang out in, but I came to see you." Her voice now reassuring.

"I just thought . . ." I stopped and looked at Deb. A sincere concern was evident on her face. "I guess I am pretty uncomfortable being here. I don't know if I would have come to visit someone in here, that's all. Thanks for coming."

"So. What's going on so far? Do you have a roommate?" Deb asked.

"I spent most of the day meeting people, and my roomy appears to be a real winner. She's downstairs in the lobby of the West Clinic with her husband. He's always here with her."

I felt displaced being on the ward. Having someone visit me seemed to intensify my sense of shame. Deb being there confirmed to her the actual fact that I was indeed on the psych ward. I was not sure how I would handle the relationship with Deb once we were back on neutral territory. Would I be able to look her in the face outside these four walls? Would she ever be able to forget? Deb's first visit, while it helped me to relate to someone on the outside, created a new set of future problems for me.

Our conversation quickly focused on Deb and how she had managed to settle in Ohio, so far away from home. She explained that the opportunities for a nurse were much better in Ohio, and while her parents were not happy with her decision, they allowed her to make up her own mind. I envied her independence.

The time quickly passed, as the two-hour visiting period came to an end. I walked her to the end of the hall, telling her, "Deb, I really appreciate your coming. I actually felt human for a while, forgot where I was. Thank you. I really mean that."

As Deb stood at the door, she said, "I'll see you again tomorrow night. Don't let them get you down. It's hard, but give it some time." She put her arms around me in a gentle embrace as she said once again, softly, "I'll see you tomorrow," and was gone.

October thirty-first—Halloween. Spooks and goblins, children and laughter. Excitement grows until the time comes for the children to ring that first door bell, to yell "Trick or treat," loving the feeling of being afraid and hoping someone would take them by surprise and scare the hell out of them. Yet for some children Halloween is a scary time. It is a time to take refuge behind their mothers as all the ghosts and monsters invade their home. They are afraid of what they don't understand. They know that if they wander too far away from mother, something terrible, something ugly, cold, and chilling will grab them. I was one of those children.

As a child, I was afraid to watch all the scary movies on television. If my sisters insisted on watching a monster movie, I would sit quietly with my eyes closed and my fingers in my ears. I was never brave, always afraid to go into dark rooms, and I always imagined that things would get me. The light of day meant safety; the night was threatening and uncertain. I reacted that way to being alone until about a year after I was married.

Now I was again faced with the unknown. Alone on a ward with all the other psych patients I feared that they would start grabbing and clutching at me, that they would somehow be transformed into monsters right before my eyes—the same monsters that I had been afraid of most of my life. This time, however, there was no place to hide. I could not put my fingers in my ears and close my eyes and pretend they weren't there. I was an adult. Adults are supposed to have self-control and to brave the dark without any signs of fear. I should be able to meet fear head on.

Shortly after Deb left, about eight o'clock, I was told to go back to the lounge, a room two doors down from mine filled with chairs and couches, a room filled with those crazy people. There I sat, in the middle of it all, pretending none of it bothered me but wanting to scream and run as far away as possible. I sat there, frozen, waiting to see what was going to happen, uncertain that I would react appropriately.

It turned out to be a Halloween party for the patients on the ward. They were trying to make the most of a very bad situation. Their efforts did not help me, however. Being in such close proximity to the other patients created an uneasy feeling in the pit of my stomach.

My heart started pounding when I saw two middle-aged women jump on a young, red-headed, freckle-faced boy, and tickle him. Everyone was laughing. They thought this carrying on was funny! Even the nurse on duty was laughing, not even attempting to stop it. No one seemed concerned. All I could think of was that this might go too far, get out of hand and turn into an ugly scene. I was afraid we would all be locked in our rooms for the night for being unruly. Flashbacks to *Cuckoo's Nest*.

But nothing happened! Everyone was in control. They knew when to stop. Soon everyone was back in their seats, ready to celebrate. Apprehensive that something else might happen, I became very tense and waited for another outburst, for one of them to pounce on me. I watched every move anyone made. I sat in my seat like a statue and tried to remain calm. That night proved to be the scariest Halloween of my life!

Shortly after the Halloween party was over, one of the patients came to my room and without knocking, walked in and said in a distant, unemotional voice, "You have a phone call."

As I reached the pay phone at the end of the hall, I picked it up, waiting for the person on the other end to say something. I became angry knowing anyone could listen as I talked on the phone. No matter where I went, someone was always watching, listening, judging me.

"Penney." Scott's voice was hurried. A sense of duty filled his voice. "Sorry I'm calling so late. I know I should have called earlier but I didn't get home till six-thirty and Scotty was waiting for me to take him out trick-or-treating."

Without emotion in my voice, I replied, "That's okay, it doesn't matter."

"Come on, Penney." A moment of silence followed. I waited for him to continue. "Penney? Penney, how are you?" Without waiting for an answer, he said, "Scotty had a great time tonight. He got all kinds of candy."

"Make sure you check it before he eats it." Still no emotion in my voice.

"I did."

"Scott," I said, about ready to commit myself to some emotion.

"What?" The voice at the other end of the phone replied hopefully.

"Nothing." My voice empty.

"Penney I got to go. I'll call you tomorrow night. I'm still planning on driving up Friday afternoon, so I'll see you then. Take care of yourself." His voice was now more sincere. His concern more apparent. "I love you."

"Okay. See you then." A pause as my mind tried unsuccessfully to find words to end the conversation with a promise of hope for the two of us. "Good night."

I did not realize then that I had been very angry at Scott. I saw him as the one who had put me there-there on 7-B with the crazy people. I felt as if he had betrayed me. He promised to love me in sickness and in health, not to lock me up when things got too far out of hand. If he really loved me he would not have placed me there.

NOVEMBER 1, THURSDAY

"Penney, it's time to get up." A distant voice, harsh and
scratchy, infiltrated my restless sleep.

Where am I? Who is that? Oh my God I remember.

My eyes, still not able to focus clearly, saw only a blurry
outline of Stella standing at the door saying, "If you don't
get up and get moving, you won't be back from breakfast in
time for group."

Slowly and painfully, with a great deal of effort, I got up
and forced myself to shower. I put off washing my hair for
another day. It was already the second day, and nothing had
changed. I still struggled against pain to snap snaps, zipper
zippers, and button the buttons in an attempt to get dressed.
As I brushed my hair, a gnawing pain in my arms grew with
each stroke. Reluctantly I went to breakfast, alone.

Even though we were meant to be separate, the pain patients still had to participate in the overall routine of the ward.
The same ward as the psych patients. There were two parts
of their schedule by which we had to abide. One was what
they called "recreational therapy." Last night's festivities were
an example of that. The other started at 8:30 a.m. sharp! It
was referred to as "ward government."

I was in the lounge getting a cup of coffee, but planning
to go back to my room. There I could sit quietly and try to
gain some control of the overpowering pain that was envelop-
ing me.

"This meeting will come to order," said the elderly man
who sat alone on the couch at the far end of the room. His
voice was demanding, filled with authority. "Miss, you over
there at the coffee pot, please sit down. We are ready to start
the meeting."

Without answering, I found a seat in the corner of the room
and sat my coffee on the arm of the chair. I reached in my
pocket for a cigarette. "There will be *no smoking* during this

meeting!'' The man's voice came at me again, stronger, louder. ''Can we please have order in here?'' His voice still demanding silence in the room. ''First the secretary will read the minutes from the last meeting. Madam secretary.''

A small, frail woman stood up and began reading from a paper in her hands. The paper quivered as she read. When she stopped reading, she let out a sigh of relief and sat down.

''Are there any additions or corrections to the minutes?'' Mr. Gentry, the president, looked around the room, his expression arrogant as he looked squarely at each person in the room. ''If there are no corrections, the minutes stand approved as read.''

The room was silent, no one willing to say anything. I sat waiting, wondering what was going on. He went through a list of things the patients were to do: a movie, bingo prizes from the previous night, and elections of new officers.

''Now for the elections. Every two weeks we must elect new officers. Tomorrow will be my last meeting as president. I want to thank all of you for making my term so enjoyable. I will miss it.'' A note of sadness and sincerity came through as he spoke. ''Nominations are now open for president.''

Each person sitting in the room hesitated to speak until one woman, sitting next to me, spoke up. ''I nominate you again, Mr. President,'' putting an accent on ''Mr. President.''

With no reaction to her nomination, he asked, ''Are there any others?''

One other person had been nominated for president. The nominations went on until they reached treasurer. I had the misfortune of being one of the chosen, and when I declined, I was told, ''You cannot decline a nomination.''

Once all nominations were made, the president said, ''We will have the ballot box out all day. Please place your ballots in there before dinner time. We will post the winners tonight. Good luck to you all.'' Glancing over at Rod, the aid who monitored the meeting, he asked, ''Is there anything else.''

''Nope.'' Relief in his voice that it was over.

"I call this meeting adjourned." He banged his hand on the table in front of him. The president had spoken!

I quickly got up and left the room, thinking, I was at the wrong place at the wrong time *again!*

Unfortunately, I was elected treasurer. I carried out my duties without really getting involved with any of the psych patients. But I was the only pain patient who attended the meetings. The reason? I was told I had to.

"Does everyone know each other?" Stella asked as she walked into the lounge, the silk scarf she wore around her neck gently touching her head. "Ed won't be able to be with us this morning, but I can get you started." She sat in a chair away from the rest of us as she proceeded. "Let's see, I know that Penney and Suzy know each other, but I don't think you two have met Jim."

"Howdy!" Jim smiled at us, making evident his missing front tooth.

I could picture Jim in the mountains of West Virginia, living in a log cabin with a plain and simple wife and a dozen kids running around barefoot through the mud, which they called a yard. Jim was sitting on the porch in the old oak rocker handed down from his grandpappy, puffing away at his corn cob pipe. Jim was a hillbilly from head to toe and had all the mannerisms that went along with it. He was very laid back and low keyed. I couldn't imagine that his pain would get in the way of rocking in his chair hour after hour.

My thoughts were broken as Stella began. "This is the first real group of pain patients on this unit. Dr. Covington and I have worked hard to get your schedule prepared. If you have any questions about what you are supposed to do, just come and ask me." Stella stopped to sip at her coffee. Her eyes moved slowly around the room as she examined each one of us with her fixed stare. She was silent, motionless as she watched, patiently anticipating conversation to get underway.

Each of us—Jim, Suzy, and myself—sat solemnly. Our eyes shifted from Stella to the floor as the silence continued for ten minutes. It was Stella who finally broke the hush of the room with, "You know, the way this is supposed to work is that you, all of you, talk to each other. Talk about your feelings. Share thoughts about how you feel." Her voice was now reaching for the right word, her expression frustrated. "I would think what you have all gone through over the past years would certainly have stirred some kind of emotion in you. Don't you have any," the word any being drawn out, "feelings about how the pain has intruded on your life?"

Still no comment from the group. Stella was willing once again to allow a lingering silence to hang over the room. Time was standing still as my mind tried unsuccessfully to focus on emotions. The only one I could even recognize was fear, and it wasn't fear of the pain, it was fear of this place, 7-B.

"I," Stella again broke the silence, "would be mad as hell if my life were so controlled by pain that I couldn't even be human anymore! Don't you people feel anything?" Stella's own anger now infiltrated her words.

"Well," Suzy began, "I guess I am mad. I don't know. I just want to know what is wrong with me. To be able to enjoy being with Sam again. Sam, he's my husband." A deep sigh of regret burst out of her as she said, "I am just getting to a point in my life when there are few responsibilities, a time for us to retire and enjoy the life we have left. Right now I can't do that." Suzy was now trying to hold back tears.

Without commenting on Suzy's remarks, Stella turned to me and asked, "What about you, Penney?"

"I don't know. Fixing my eyes on the floor," I quietly continued, "All I want to do is get better. I have too much left undone to settle for pain the rest of my life. But I don't know how. I guess that's why I'm here. I have to learn." I truly could not understand how this conversation about emotions could help me to live with my pain. It would only create more pain.

The anger I had felt the previous night toward Scott was now tucked tightly away in my mind. At that moment I could not think of anything that made me angry. Even anger I felt because of the pain, the unanswered questions, the sheer frustration of the past six years did not come to mind as I sat with the others waiting for Stella to lead us.

The next hour and a half was spent in superficial talk about feelings we probably all had but were unwilling to talk about or recognize. Disgusted, Stella ended the group meeting as she said, "I have a book. You are all required to read it. It's called *The Angry Book*." She pulled three books out of a bag that lay beside her chair. She handed one to each of us. "You will have time in the evening to read this. It should only take about two or three days to finish. Maybe then we can have an honest conversation about anger." Stella paused for a moment, eyeing each of us, her glare penetrating as she proceeded. "The issue here is to recognize feelings. Those feelings *do* have an effect on your pain. Anger is a part of that. If you aren't more willing to talk when Ed is in group . . ." She stopped in midsentence, unwilling to express her view as she glanced at her watch. "It's time for you to go down to sports medicine. Oh, Suzy, you'd better not go; you have another test. Just go wait in your room. Someone will come and get you. Jim, you show Penney the way down."

I followed Jim out of the room and down the long dreary hall of 7-B feeling angry, frustrated, and hopeless, my anger now surfacing at Jim and Suzy just because they were a part of this pain unit and all it stood for. Although they were in 7-B for the same reason I was, I saw them as that part of the unit, which represented both isolation from the outside world and intrusion on my thoughts and actions. My morning had gone badly, and that made both Suzy and Jim seem all the more threatening to me. I placed them in the same category as every other patient on this floor—crazy. I was angry for being there, for the pain I had had to bear for six years, and for the pain and torment I would probably have to continue to bear.

Without revealing any of my feelings about my fellow group members, I followed closely behind Jim, who had been on the unit for several weeks already. I had no other choice. As we entered the large room, a gymnasium of sorts, I saw that each weight-lifting apparatus was being manipulated by strong, apparently physically fit people. All my initial fears and doubts about the pain program returned. My first reaction was to block out what I saw: muscular men straining, their faces filled with determination, sweat pouring down their brows. All of their muscles were well defined, protruding from their backs and arms. Their sweat made their bulging biceps shine in the fluorescent lighting. Each one was able to persevere through the demanding physical routine.

Jim went directly into his own routine. He was familiar with the smaller pieces of equipment placed in the center of the room. It was with these smaller, less demanding pieces that I would be expected to work. Without any difficulty, Jim began lifting the bar attached to the chain. As I watched him, I could see small black weights raised off the floor. Up and down with a clanging metal sound went the chain as Jim's eyes were filled with the same determination, the same strain as the others in this sweat shop.

As I stood by quietly watching him, I heard a voice come from behind me saying, "Penney, how are you this morning?" It was Rita, whom I had met briefly the day before. She would be in charge of my physical therapy.

Startled, I turned around to face her, saying, "Oh! I don't know about this."

"Don't worry about those other people. The Clinic has a health club—this place—which employees of the Clinic can use. A lot of them come down here to work out. Even the Cleveland Browns use it sometimes. I won't expect you to keep pace with them." A smile appeared on her face. She shifted her clipboard from one hand to the other as she said, "We do, however, expect you to follow the program we lay out for you. I have gone over your records this morning at the staff meeting, and you have been cleared to work on all this equipment. You are physically able," she chuckled as she continued, "but are you willing?"

"Yeah. I guess so." I said with an undertone of doubt.

I followed closely behind Rita as she walked toward a strange apparatus. It was a long, narrow table, covered in red vinyl and shaped like the oversized stool that shoe salesmen use. The front end sloped downward and had metal bars coming across from either side. These bars were parallel to the floor, and each one supported a flat disk-shaped weight.

"Get up here and sit down, let your legs hang over the edge." Rita commanded.

I climbed up on the table and slid my bottom toward the sloped end of the table, my legs hanging over the edge, my ankles resting on the bar that supported the weights. "Okay, that's right. Now put your feet under these two bars." Rita helped me place my feet under the two parallel bars. "Good."

"I'll put it on ten pounds for you. That should be a good place for you to start. You can lift ten pounds can't you?" Rita was standing over me as she continued, "Just pull your legs up away from the table's edge, like you are going to straighten your leg. See how far you can get the bar up. It should be easy." No doubt at all in her voice as she spoke.

Try as I did, I could not even move the bar. "I . . . I can't seem to get this thing moving," I told Rita, embarrassed, unable to look at her as I spoke.

Without saying anything, Rita bent down and pulled the two five-pound disklike weights off of the machine. "There," she said briskly as she stepped back. "See if you can at least lift the bar."

I was able to pull the weight of the metal bar up a little and Rita said, disbelieving, "Well, at least we know you can lift the bar." She stopped to make a note on her clipboard before continuing, this time in a more understanding tone, "All right, good. I realize this is difficult for you. You are out of shape, but that's okay, I'll help you. Sometimes I ex-

pect too much from you guys.'' She was referring to the pain
patients. "You look so good. Most of my patients have braces,
walkers, canes. They don't come strolling into sports medicine
on their own two feet looking normal. I have to remind myself
sometimes that even though you guys look good, this stuff
is difficult for you, too. We'll work together on the rest. Deal?''
A smile now appeared on her face.

"Deal.'' I replied, relieved.

For the next thirty minutes Rita and I worked together on
six different pieces of equipment. In spite of my inability to
lift more than five pounds on any one piece, Rita was
understanding.

"Well, Penney, by the time you leave here you will be
able to lift at least fifteen pounds on every one of these. That
is a promise!'' Her determination to meet the challenge I
presented was clearly evident.

"I hope so.'' My voice was hollow as I spoke. "I guess I'll
see you this afternoon for physical therapy.''

Rita nodded her head as she turned to leave. I watched
her walk out, so healthy, so young, so able to meet the physical
demands life put on her. I knew in my heart that I had not
put out 100 per cent that day. Dr. Gabis's doubts still lingered
in my mind. "They could have missed something'' echoed
in my head as I followed Jim back to the ward, exhausted,
discouraged, and frightened. Would I make it?

As Jim stepped into the elevator at 7-B I could feel my
legs trembling, not out of fear, but out of exhaustion. I had
been on the move all day, not stopping for a moment. Lying
down even for a few minutes was discouraged by the staff as
exhibiting pain behavior. Naturally I interpreted that as forbidden. With my legs feeling like rubber, I stepped off the
elevator at the lobby of the West Clinic. I assumed we would
be having PT in the same area as sports medicine.

"No! Not there.'' Jim grabbed me by the arm as I turned
into sports medicine. "This time it ain't so easy to get thar.
We got some walkin' to do.''

There was a skywalk off the West Clinic lobby that connected that part of the building to the Main Clinic. I remembered going that way with Stella when I was admitted. I actually liked the skywalk, with its floor-to-ceiling windows. I enjoyed the light, airy feeling I got when there was nothing to restrict my view. In the coming weeks I would spend many quiet moments on this skywalk, lagging behind the group, just looking out the windows, letting the sun warm me, wondering, hoping, feeling brief moments of freedom. As Jim and I reached the Main Clinic building on the other side of the walk, the feeling of freedom faded as the institutional green tile walls met my eyes. The Main Clinic building had a red line running down the middle of the hall floor to direct people to the main elevator bank. ''Just follow the red line'' was a comment the guards must have tired of saying.

"Here." Jim stopped at a bank of elevators marked Employees Only. "This here is what we gotta take." His voice was so calm and unaffected by the unyielding day.

"We can't! It says for employees," I said, concerned.

"The hell with that. You wanta walk another ten minutes to get there? Come on, I've been doing this for weeks, nobody stopped me yet." Jim's voice sounded irritated as he continued. "I ain't gonna walk no more. You come with me now!"

I was shocked by his firmness. I followed him into the elevator. We rode in silence to the eighth floor and walked down the hall to the end, where Jim stopped at a counter, saying politely, "We are here to see Rita."

The girl at the desk said, "Go on back. She's waiting for you." Jim headed through another hallway into a large open room before she finished her sentence.

God, will it never end? I thought as I entered the room. This room was filled with gym mats hung along both sides of the wall. The patients, some with only one leg, or one arm, their bodies twisted and distorted, were lying on what looked like a waterbed frame cushioned by one of the mats. The physical therapist worked patiently with the unfortunate souls as they attempted to get their bodies moving. My physically able appearance now seemed more apparent than ever; I was at least standing on my own two feet.

"It's about time you got here." Rita said jokingly as she walked up to Jim, giving me a quick "how do you do" glance. "You guys ready? Where is Suzy?"

"Another test," Jim replied, his tone reflecting his annoyance with Suzy.

"Oh well, let's get started." Rita headed toward the middle of the floor and pulled some mats off the wall. Jim gave her a hand and placed them on the floor. I stood silently by.

"Okay." Rita stopped and looked directly at me, placing her hands on her hips, letting out a sigh as she said, "Penney, do you know why we are doing this?"

"No. Well . . . it's supposed to help me feel better?" Disbelief filled my voice.

"Believe it or not that's true. One problem we find with most pain patients is their lack of movement. They sit or lie down all day, and their muscles get weaker and weaker as each day passes. If we are to help you, we have to begin by toning up your body to get those muscles back to where they should be. In fact, as you progress and build up more tone in your muscles, you will probably experience less pain." She looked at me, anticipating some reaction, her desire to help evident.

"I guess it could be so," I said still not convinced.

"Just ask Jim. The first week he was here, he could hardly walk to PT on his own. He had to use a cane. Now look at him." Rita turned to Jim, flexed her arm muscles, imitating a strong man, and continued. "In the three weeks that he has been here he has managed to progress tenfold. He's really done well. You'll see in time."

How in the world could I go from nothing to over a full hour of exercise and weight lifting? As Rita went through each exercise with me, sit-ups, leg lifts, side bends, arm circles, even walking up and down stairs, I found it impossible to believe I was helping my body. Each movement was more difficult than the one before. Pain radiated to every joint and muscle as, only halfheartedly, I followed Rita and Jim through the routine.

By the time we were finished almost forty-five minutes later, all I could think of was getting to bed. I wanted to lie down for a few minutes, just long enough to compose myself. I wanted to believe there was hope for me in this program, but as I followed Jim back to 7-B, depression and failure filled my thoughts.

By four o'clock I was back in my room, trying to anticipate the next move and telling myself I had made it through at least one day. Every muscle in my body was throbbing with pain.

NOVEMBER 1, THURSDAY

"Squeeze my finger. . . . Stand up. . . . Hold your arms out and close your eyes. . . . Now touch your nose. . . . Let me see you walk. . . . Stand up straight and close your eyes. . . . Am I turning your toes up or down? . . . Can you feel this?" He was young and rather good looking, tall and slender. Hair black as coal set off his deep blue eyes. I gazed into his eyes hoping to find someone who would understand me and realize how great my pain was and how much I wanted to rid myself of it. But I saw nothing. He was still a doctor, and he used the same words, the same tests, and the same perplexing expressions.

I didn't have to know him to know what he was thinking. How could he take me seriously? Everything could easily be explained by my presence on that ward. In my heart I felt I had been given a label that would follow me for the rest of my life. It would stand in the way of objective medical treatment. It was too easy to use my mental state as a universal answer. I had placed this mental-patient label on myself, and I was convinced that others used it, too. There was no doubt in my mind that this young, knowledgeable physician was thinking precisely the same thing.

Two days after that examination I was informed that the neurologist found nothing irregular. Aside from the pain in my joints caused by the fibrositis, there was no nerve damage or on-going tissue destruction. The only "real" pain was in the connective tissues in my extremities. What's more, they had no conclusive explanation for that sort of pain. They knew it existed, but little else. No form of quick treatment would make it disappear. Medication, reduced stress, and above all, exercise was all they could offer me. When I heard that, I didn't believe it. I was in much greater pain than when I had arrived and I knew that the exercise had caused it.

My last hope of being acquitted had been taken away. I had to accept the facts. If they didn't think I was capable of following the program, I would not be there. If they thought I would injure myself by lifting weights, they wouldn't ask me to. I would have to lift those weights and stretch my body until I collapsed. I would have to accept the pain these activities would create and say nothing. I would have to suffer in silence, but that didn't help me believe the pain would ever go away.

"Someone get down here right now! Do you hear me?" The words came flying at me from the hall. "Come on people! Come on!" I caught a quick glimpse of the woman as she passed my door.

One of the nurses approached the screaming woman saying, "Please Mrs. Gentry, will you keep your voice down." The nurse reached out her hand to Mrs. Gentry.

"No! I want something done immediately! Yesterday my husband was fine and today he can't even get up to go to the bathroom." Her voice slowly faded as the nurse managed to move her into a nearby room.

By the time I reached the hallway there was no one in sight. A dead silence hung in the air. Suddenly Mrs. Gentry burst out into the hall yelling at the top of her lungs once more. "You people are not fooling anyone! My husband is an important man and you treat him like trash. He has needs. You have not helped him from what I can see. He can't even talk to me. He just lies there looking into space."

The nurse, once again trying to regain control of the situation, interjected, "Please Mrs. Gentry, I would really like you to lower your voice."

"I'll lower my voice when you people get off your ass and do something for my husband!"

This time the nurse was assisted by one of the orderlies. They took her by the hand and lead her down the hall and out the door. They disappeared from sight, but I could still hear Mrs. Gentry's voice, "What is wrong with you?" and the voice was gone.

I never did find out what had happened to cause such a commotion. Mrs. Gentry's loud voice did, however, upset me. I wondered if any patients would lose control. What was to prevent one of them from going off the deep end? If they could not control a patient's wife, how in the world would they ever be able to control a patient if the need arose?

NOVEMBER 2, FRIDAY

As I opened my eyes and took in that first deep breath of the morning, I could feel the intensity of my pain send waves of alarm through my body. Not one muscle in my body was pain free. Muscles I never knew existed ached intensely. It was only my sheer determination that allowed me to gain some control over my body and get out of bed. I felt as if I had been hit with a ten-ton truck, each muscle responding to the crushing impact. I was also unable to think clearly because my head felt as if it would burst any minute. The exercise from the previous day had caught up with me.

Scott was to be in group that morning. I had to conceal the degree of pain, if only for him. When he arrived, his attitude was positive, as usual. He still believed I would get

better, not worse. Although I was discouraged, I wasn't ready
to see him give up. Maybe my pain would lessen if I got my
mind on something else.

When Scott and I arrived, Stella, coffee cup in hand, was
already in the room across the hall from 7-B where group was
held. There was only one video unit for 7-B so, the pain patients used this room on Monday, Wednesday, and Friday and
the psych patients used it the other days. The video tape en-
abled the entire staff to watch our group at their convenience,
to spy on our personal discussions and to translate our words
and actions into their own definition of "normal." It allowed
them to watch for pain behavior, signs that without words told
others we were in pain, like rubbing one's forehead, grabbing
one's back when standing, holding one's self stiff.

As we walked into the room, Stella had a cheery greeting
for us, saying, "Good morning. I am glad to see that you made
it back to Cleveland, Scott. It is really important for you to
be as involved in this program as you can be."

Placing her coffee cup on the table, she went about her
business of preparing the video camera, moving chairs, shifting the camera, looking into the view finder, and placing the
camera so that it would easily film everyone in the room.

"What is that for?" Scott asked Stella, his tone relaxed,
comfortable in spite of being one of the subjects for the camera.

Stopping what she was doing, Stella looked up at Scott
and said, "We find that our patients don't always pick up
on everything in group. Their minds wander, their thoughts
aren't always on what is being said." Pausing for a sip of
coffee, Stella explained, "One of the most important contri-
butions these video tapes make is that they give patients an
opportunity to see themselves as others see them. They can
watch what they look like, their mannerisms, the way they
talk, their expressions. They will watch this tape tonight, after
visiting hours, with the night pain nurse and then have a
discussion." Affirming her belief, she confidently said, "I
think what happens here in this group is by far the most im-

portant part of the program, and this taping gives them a double dose, so to speak.''

Dr. Covington walked in and headed for the desk chair against the far wall. He slid comfortably into the chair, and, without saying anything, began to look at each of us. No words were spoken, only uncomfortable glances and blank looks. Minutes passed before he spoke, solicitude in his voice. ''The only way this group is going to help any of you is if you begin to open up, share a part of yourself with the group. Allow your feelings to come freely and openly without shutting them off. I realize this is a difficult situation for all of you, but as the days go by you will feel more comfortable with each other, more trusting.''

Once again he paused to study each of us as we sat quietly, willing to let him do all the talking. My eyes never met his, but I could feel him looking at me, feel his eyes, studying me. Was he reading my mind? Could he do such a thing? Many times in the weeks to come I would ask myself the same question.

The silence in the room became uncomfortable. With each passing moment the deafening silence intensified. Suzy shifted in her seat, Sam's breathing penetrated the stillness. Stella's lighter echoed as she lit her cigarette. The longer the hush continued, the more difficult it became for me even to think of speaking. Now none of us was willing to break the silence. I watched the clock on the wall as it ticked away seconds, hoping someone, anyone, would say something.

What felt like hours but was in reality only ten minutes of dead silence was broken by Dr. Covington. Now irritated with our lack of participation, he said, ''Why are you people here?'' My eyes met his as he continued, ''Penney, what did you expect to accomplish here?''

With a quiver in my voice I responded, ''I . . . I came here to get help. To . . . to . . . have you help me feel better, I guess.''

''You guess! Don't you know?'' A bit of amusement filled his voice.

"Yes, you are going to help me," my tone firmer this time. My head pounded. With each word I spoke, the motion of my jaw intensified the pain like an army marching over my brain.

Dr. Covington stared at me again, his eyes wide, his expression doubtful as he said, "You know there is nothing *I* can do to help you?" My eyes narrowed as I heard his words. "What you are going to get out of this program is the total amount of what *you* put into it. It is up to *you* to work toward a better understanding of who you are, what your needs are, what benefits you gain from your pain. Then *you* will have to sort it all out. You must be willing to talk with me, the staff, and the other people in your group in order to reach your goal."

Once again silence prevailed as each of us thought about what had just been said. Finally Jim spoke up, a seriousness in his voice I had heard before. "I know exactly what Dr. Covington is talking about. I been here longer than you two. I've been talkin' with him and the nurses about 'lot of stuff. Ain't no one knows better than me what I need. I thought this program was a bunch of hogwash when I first got here. But now I see that all this stuff is really important. I talk a lot to Dr. Covington and he helps me figure some things out I never understood. I ain't sayin' I know exactly where I'm head'n, but I got a much better idear of what I need. And I feel a lot better now than when I first came in here." Jim's words were sincere, his attitude positive, his need to reach out to Suzy and me evident as he continued. "Ain't no one gonna do nothin' for you less you make the first move. You got to make the first move."

Dr. Covington looked Jim's way with a smile of approval on his lips as he added, "I think that about says it all. If you really try to help yourself, the staff is going to be there for you." Dr. Covington stopped a moment, put his fingers together as he thought. His expression changed several times before he continued. "I hope that this group will be able to be open, work together. You know that it is often the case that you, the group, can help each other more than the rest of the staff put together.''

Group had proven to be more thought provoking than I had anticipated. As Dr. Covington ended the group that morning, I felt a small hope flicker inside of me. Jim's attitude toward the program had also helped. Perhaps I might be able to engineer the same kind of positive attitude toward the program. Time would tell. I was still very new to the program, and although I felt I had gained insight into what this unit was all about, I still had a very long, painful road to travel.

Scott left shortly after group was over and returned that night for visiting hours. I didn't know what he had planned to entertain himself with all day, and somehow it didn't matter to me. Even though I had, at that moment a positive attitude about the program, I could feel myself pulling emotionally away from him. I struggled not to show the intense pain I felt in my head with each word, as I said, "See you tonight. Meet me in my room about seven." Without any further words, I turned and left him standing there in the hall, an expression of bewilderment on his face. I had not even given him a kiss good-bye.

Pain was now the center of my thoughts for the rest of the day, as I could feel the blood pulsing through my head with each step I took. I told myself if I had asked for an aspirin before going to sports medicine, I would have put myself into the role of a patient. I went to sports medicine, my head pounding as if it would burst at any moment.

The intensity of my headache did not let up at all during the day. I felt distant from everything around me, as the haze of unrelieved pain continued. I concentrated every ounce of effort on making it through the day without drawing attention to myself or my inability to control my pain. I didn't care how I did it, I just wanted to get the day over with.

Visiting hours that day were difficult for me. I became distant with Scott, not only because of my confusion, but because
it was far too difficult to concentrate on anything, preoccupied
as I was with waves of pain. Deb had accompanied Scott to
the Clinic that evening. I became the silent partner in a triangle
of idle conversation. Awkward moments seemed to linger in
the air as Scott and Deb tried unsuccessfully to involve me
in their discussions. Finally it was time for them to leave.

"Well, I'll see you tomorrow for group. About nine
o'clock, right?" Scott said as he pulled me close to him, placing his lips gently on my forehead.

"Okay. I'll see you then." My words were low, unclear
as Scott tightened his embrace, as if he was unwilling to let
me go.

That evening Joan, the pain nurse on the three-to-eleven
shift, came into my room. She was young and attractive, and
was dressed in what I considered an unusual manner for a
nurse: baggy pants, bold yellow flowers on the loosely fitted
blouse, and high heeled boots. We had just returned to our
rooms ten minutes earlier from viewing the tape of the group.
Joan wanted to know what I thought of the tape.

"I didn't like it," I replied, feeling each word reverberating
in ripples of pain through my head.

"Did you notice anything about yourself?"

I had noticed a lot, none of it constructive. I didn't think
she wanted to spend time with all the trivia, so I asked, perplexed, "What do you mean?"

"I noticed that when you talked, you never once moved
your mouth." She was not attacking me, but I felt as if she
were.

"I never really thought about it." I could even hear the
hurt in my voice.

I just wanted her to leave my room and let me be. I did
not want to focus on such a small, unimportant matter. But
she wasn't ready to leave. She had more to say. "It looked
to me as if you were trying to hold back, to keep something,

some feeling, inside of you." She paused for a minute to watch my reaction. "I think that if you begin to recognize what you are feeling and express those feelings, you might notice on the next tape that you are improving. You aren't going to change things overnight, but you have to begin with small steps. Ask yourself what you were feeling during that particular group."

I answered in a low, almost ashamed, tone, "I was confused, scared. I don't know about this program." My head still throbbing, I tried to keep my mind on the issue.

Joan looked at me, her wide brown eyes filled with sensitivity. "I can understand that. You have been through a lot these past six years, but your life can be better, if you want." Her tone was as empathetic and consoling as her expression. "All we can ask is that you try to help yourself. Work with us and allow us to try to help you. I know that there are a lot of confusing things right now going on inside of you. And you'll probably become more confused before things begin to get clear. But I believe that if you can think back to today, try to recreate in your mind what you were feeling, you might recognize why you had such a need to hold back certain feelings."

Now, trusting Joan more than I should have, I broke one rule I had vowed never to break while on the pain unit and said, "I had a terrible headache. I still have one."

"Did you ask for anything?" Her voice filled with surprise. "I know you have orders written for a mild pain pill if you really need it. I'll go get you one. If you need any more just go ask the nurse at the desk." She got up from the chair and was gone.

I didn't want to take a pill. I knew the kinds of reactions I had had in the past. But just this one time, only one might not hurt.

NOVEMBER 3, SATURDAY MORNING

Damn the pain . . . still there. No, it's not fair. Can't stay
in bed. Must get up. Why? Why? Why? I'm trying. I'm trying. Got to get another pain pill, just one to take the edge
off. Got to feel good for Scott. It's going to be a long day.
Joan said it was okay to take a pain pill. It's okay. I'm not
weak for taking one, just one. I hurt. What a strange feeling.
I'm floating, removed from everything. Are my feet touching
the floor? Things are just . . . no real substance. How easy
to feel like this, no pain, no cares, just being. Is this what they
meant by living with pain? Nothing is real. Cafeteria isn't
bad . . . just there . . . distant . . . out of reach, yet so near.
Coffee . . . that will fix me up . . . coffee. Got to get back
to group. I feel the weight of my body returning. Must be
the coffee . . . still strange, but . . . I can feel the floor
now . . . damn pills. The pain was so bad. They took the edge
off.

Shortly after group Dr. Covington made rounds. He
wanted to talk with each of us before we left on a pass for
the day.

"Why are you taking those pain pills?" He asked as he
glanced down at my chart. "You have gone six years without
them, why now?"

I could not tell him the reason I really took those pills.
That would mean describing my tremendous pain to him. I
would have to tell him how difficult the program was and how
uncertain I was of making it there. I could not tell him I was
afraid of the pain itself, afraid that I was getting worse, afraid
they had missed something in all their tests. No, I couldn't
tell him what I was feeling.

"I thought just once wouldn't hurt. I'm sorry." My voice
sounded like that of a child being scolded by a concerned
parent. I knew it would never happen again.

I took everything so seriously, every little remark made to
me while on 7-B seemed to me to be gospel those first few
weeks. I believed every word Dr. Covington and Dr. Gabis

said. My only hope lay with them, and my need for a total recovery was so strong that I was willing to do just as they said, no matter how painful it would prove to be for me. I felt frightened knowing that in the days to come I would endure prolonged pain, but my need to get better far outweighs my need for short-term relief through pills.

Before Dr. Covington left my room he suggested, jokingly of course, that I go play tennis. For some reason his comment made me feel capable of enjoying the day. In the past, all the doctors ever told me was to stop doing, never suggesting I do anything "normal." One day at a time, I thought. I might, with luck, survive the place after all.

NOVEMBER 3, SATURDAY AFTERNOON

When Scott and I left the West Clinic building, the warmth of the sun delighted me as we walked hand-in-hand to the car. A gentle breeze tossed my hair about, adding to my sense of freedom. For the first time since I had entered 7-B, I felt unrestricted, uninhibited, willing to drop my defenses momentarily.

As Scott and I drove away I looked at the hospital ID band hanging loosely around my left wrist and wondered if people on the street would sense my well-guarded secret: 7-B-the psych ward.

With the chill of winter just barely noticeable, a small cluster of people stood at the bus stop, patiently waiting for the bus. I had a momentary impulse to jump out of the car, fade into the group of free people, and pretend I was also a free spirit, but I didn't. I had doubts about my decision to leave the Clinic. My room there, only three days after entering it, now represented security for me. I was afraid to expose myself to "normal" people, of someone discovering I was a psych patient. In reality, there was absolutely no way anyone could know about 7-B unless I told them. But I felt certain it was written all over my face. It would be reflected in my action and my words. I was afraid I would not be able to conceal my self-doubt, shame, and fear.

Scott took me to a nearby mall, but the fear of being discovered was in my mind incessantly as the afternoon wore on. During the entire time Scott and I spent together he remained positive, hopeful about my stay on 7-B. I envied his ability to look at life with such an upbeat attitude.

We were to return to Deb's house around five o'clock that evening to join her for dinner. She was in the kitchen, still in her nurse's uniform, when we arrived.

"You guys hungry?" Deb asked, as she walked toward the refrigerator. "Want a beer, Scott?" Deb handed him a beer, taking one for herself. "After a day like today, I need this!"

"Sure," Scott said, as he willingly took the beer.

"Penney, can I get you a Pepsi?" Deb asked.

"That's fine," I replied.

I wonder, is this what life is all about? Is eating, drinking, and idle conversation what I am trying so hard to regain? What is life really about? I always thought that my children and Scott were the most important things in my life. Are they? Who am I trying to get better for? Me? Do these two carefree people standing in front of me, casually sipping their beer, truly understand how difficult life is? How difficult life can be? How difficult life has been . . . for me?

"Dinner should be ready in about five minutes. Betty is going to join us for dinner, okay?" Deb asked politely.

Betty shared the house with Deb. I could feel the tension build in me as I prepared to meet her for the first time. Here was a stranger who very well might know what area of the Clinic I was in.

"Scott, Penney, this is Betty, my roommate. She works at the Clinic," Deb said as she motioned for us to sit down. Scott and I on one side, Betty and Deb on the other.

Betty was tiny, frail looking, no outstanding features about her. Only her hair, orange-red, prevented her from going unnoticed altogether.

Superficial conversation continued throughout dinner, as Betty sat quietly by, not once looking directly at me. Her eyes remained focused on her plate, as if her food would vanish if she glanced away, her fork rhythmically going from plate to mouth and back to her plate again. She responded only with a yes or no answer to any question directed her way. Her curious manner became increasingly more apparent as the meal progressed. Scott and Deb exchanged perplexed looks, obviously uncomfortable with Betty's lack of interaction. I immediately assumed she knew where I was staying at the Clinic and that her bizarre behavior was directed at me.

Breaking the silence, Deb said, "Why don't you guys go into the living room while I make some coffee? I'll clean this mess up later. Just give me a few minutes and the coffee will be ready."

"Don't worry about it Deb, I'll clean it up. I don't want coffee anyway. I don't mind." This was the first complete sentence uttered by Betty. Her voice was unemotional, lacking any feeling at all. "I'd rather stay in here anyway."

Scott and I walked into the living room and sat at opposite ends of the room. I asked him, "Scott, can you take me back to the Clinic now?" I felt distant from everything around me, misplaced, ill at ease.

"Now!" Scott asked, his voice surprised. "You don't have to be back for two and half hours yet. Why don't you just sit down and relax for a while." He got up and walked toward me, his eyes sad, his expression perplexed.

"No. I want to go back now. I am really tired. I had a long day. I have to be up early tomorrow morning. I think it would be a good idea if you took me back, please!" There was a sense of urgency in my voice as I spoke. My body stiffened as Scott reached out for my hand.

"If that's what you want," he said, as he took his hand away from mine.

"Yes." Weariness was apparent by my tone. I was anxious to leave that house as soon as possible.

Only the faint hum of the engine broke the dead silence that prevailed as we headed down narrow city streets toward the Clinic. Neither Scott nor I was in a talking mood. He remained silent, directing his total attention to the road. He did not have to say anything. I could see the expression on his face, in the light cast by the street lamps as we passed them. His brow was wrinkled. His mouth was turned down at the corners, an unusual expression for him. I knew I had hurt him, disappointed him by returning early. But I was unable to cope with Betty's negative vibes.

It was my own negative feeling about being on the psych ward that led me to believe her behavior was directed toward me. The same kind of assumption I had made all my life about others with whom I had contact. If I had not felt so inadequate and unimportant, I might have made some attempt to communicate with Betty in spite of her withdrawn behavior.

The silence continued as Scott and I approached the Clinic. Not until we stepped off the elevator on 7-B did I make an attempt to talk with him. His shoulders were slouched, his mood somber as I said, "I'm sorry, Scott. I'm tired. We still have tomorrow together. I'll be more rested by then." I looked into his eyes for some sign of emotion, something that would help me feel less guilty.

"Yeah, you're right. But I wanted today to go on forever. You've only been away for three days but it feels like three years to me. I'm not used to your being gone. You have always been at home for us. I kept telling myself these last few days that I would be with you this weekend, spend as much time as possible with you. I guess I'm just having trouble adjusting to your being gone." Scott's voice was filled with sadness. With a sigh in his voice, he leaned over and kissed me on the forehead, saying, "I'll see you tomorrow at nine o'clock. Okay?"

"Yeah, nine is good." My voice was empty. There was hurt in Scott's eyes, sadness in his voice, but I didn't care. As I approached my room, my heart felt empty and I was scared.

NOVEMBER 4, SUNDAY

The rest of the weekend did not go as I had hoped it would. I had been badly frightened. I experienced emotions I had never felt before. I was afraid to deal with the outside world, preferring instead to hide from it. I wanted to remain where I felt safe. But most of all, I think I wanted to hide from myself. I had lost that small glimmer of hope that I had had when I left the Clinic on Saturday morning. My defenses were once again in total control as I awaited a new week.

NOVEMBER 5, MONDAY MORNING

"So tell me how your weekend went," Dr. Covington asked, as he settled back in his usual chair. He pulled out the bottom drawer of the desk to rest his foot on it.

Not willing to share the experience I had had over the weekend, I simply nodded my head, indicating things were fine. Suzy, on the other hand, immediately responded with full details about her wonderful weekend.

Only a smile on Dr. Covington's face indicated that he had even heard her, as a hush fell over the room. You could feel the tension building, the uncertainty of the group about its direction. Both Scott and Sam had joined us that morning, fulfilling their pledge to remain involved in the program.

Minutes passed before the silence was broken by Dr. Covington, his eyes now fixed on Suzy and Sam. His expression intense, he asked, "How did you two feel when within a month they found cancer in both of you?" His manner and demeanor were sympathetic.

My eyes widened as Dr. Covington's words registered. I had been unaware of the traumatic experience Suzy had been through, and I regretted the hostility I had felt toward her once I realized what they must have suffered.

"You somehow don't believe that it is really happening. Right after Suzy had her mastectomy, they found cancer in my descending colon." Sam was a big man, overweight. He breathed heavily as he talked. His stomach moved up and down slowly, while his arms rested on his protruding belly. Sam took in another deep breath. He was very much in control of his emotions as he continued. "You're not prepared to deal with one type of cancer, let alone two. I was lucky; I feel great since I had my surgery. I've had no trace of cancer, and I've been feeling fine. Suzy's the one. She's had nothing but trouble with her health ever since her surgery."

"It didn't seem real to you until the day of the surgery, did it?" Dr. Covington questioned tenderly.

"No sir!" Sam replied, his voice now quivering, his thumb and forefinger propped under his chin, supporting his full face.

Dr. Covington's soft voice then revealed another very human part of himself as he told the group, "I remember when my wife was showing signs of a brain tumor. Even after the doctor wanted to do more tests to see if surgery would be necessary, we didn't believe it. I can remember joking about it with her. It wasn't until we were faced with the final test that the truth sank in. Somehow we all have a way of denying things that are too unpleasant for us to think about. When it finally hits us, it is very difficult to deal with."

Now I felt guilty about even being in the pain program. I hadn't had such a traumatic experience. My pain seemed minute compared to what Suzy must have gone through. The suffering, the anguish, the wondering about the unknown she must have to deal with in accepting the cold, hard fact that she had cancer. Perhaps I didn't belong there. Was I being a baby about my pain? Was my pain reason enough to justify being there?

"Suzy, did you feel guilty when you were unable to help Sam after his surgery?" Dr. Covington's question pulled me out of my thoughts.

"I suppose so, but our daughter was a great help—she took care of both of us." Suzy now calmer, was in control once again.

"Penney, how do you feel about the way your pain had affected your life?" Dr. Covington inquired.

"The pain . . . ," I cringed just saying the word, I had myself so psyched up about avoiding it altogether, "had taken control over my life." I replied cautiously, unwilling to express any deep feelings. "My life was not living. I was existing from day to day. I was desperate, that is why I am here."

Taking a moment, pulling a pen out of his pocket and scribbling on a note pad on the desk in front of him, Dr. Covington, deep in thought, hesitated before asking, "Scott, how did you feel about her pain?"

Without having to think, Scott quickly replied, "Helpless. I didn't know what to do for her anymore. We tried everything we could think of, and nothing helped. I tried to take care of her the best I could, even to protect her at times."

"Have you always treated her like a fragile object? Always stepped in when you felt it necessary?" Dr. Covington's questions were more pointed now.

"I guess I have to some extent. Mostly with her family. She has trouble telling people no." Scott stopped for a minute, a smile appeared on his face as he jokingly said, "Except me. She and I can communicate on the same level. In fact, she can be downright stubborn with me. It is only everyone else out there that seems to intimidate her so much."

Dr. Covington turned to me, a devilish look on his face, and asked, "Is Scott your white knight in shining armor? Do you let him take care of all the difficult stuff for you?"

"No! I can take care of myself. I am stronger than you think," I said, making a statement I had not meant to.

"I believe you can, too. That's why you have a good chance to succeed here. I guess I'd better watch out for your stubborn streak," he said, turning to Scott, exchanging light-hearted glances. Even Jim's expression, a trace of a smile, indicated he was listening to the conversation.

"What does all this have to do with my pain?" asked Suzy, her composure returned. "I mean, what does my ability to speak for myself have to do with how much pain I am going to have. You lost me, Dr. Covington."

"You are aware that your pain has effected every part of your life. Right?" Not waiting for Suzy to respond, he continued. "Well, if we are going to help you to control your pain, to be a person again, then we are going to have to work on every issue that goes through your mind. People are very complex, and it will take time for each of you to overcome the type of behavior you have exhibited in the past as a patient. Once we can identify you, who you really are, then we can begin to work on those areas you need to change in order to gain control. Do you understand?"

"No." Suzy fell silent for a moment. "All I understand is that I have nowhere else to go. I can't bear this pain anymore, and you did say you could help me. I guess you are the one who is going to fix me up . . . right?"

A slight smile appeared on Dr. Covington's face as he said, "No. I am going to help you to help yourself. It is going to be up to you to help yourself. The ball is in your court, Suzy."

The time had gone quickly that morning in group as Dr. Covington stood up, straightened his sports coat, and gathered up his pen and empty coffee cup, saying, "This group has a lot of potential. I have discovered some interesting things about some of you this morning. But what amazes me is that none of you have brought up the issue of anger. I would be mad as hell if I had to put up with all the crap you have to. You seem unaffected by the hand dealt to you. Give it some thought today. I'll see you guys back in the lounge for group tomorrow morning.

I left group that morning feeling further from controlling my pain or from having any kind of understanding of myself or my life. Pain was not the only issue here.

The video playback was in need of repair that night, so I was spared the agony of reliving the morning's group. I would not have to face the awful replay for the remainder of my stay—it was never repaired.

NOVEMBER 5, MONDAY EVENING

Angry? Not me! Maybe sad, hurt, put upon, completely burned out, exhausted from the struggle-but not angry! Anger is bad—a demon that lives within and if allowed will take over the control needed to be gentle and kind. For people like myself, who needed constant stroking, anger had to be ignored. I had to deny such feelings and never allow them to show. I had seen angry people, and they frightened me with their loud and uncontrollable rage. They were so one-sided, it was impossible to reason with them or even to calm them down. No, I could not allow myself to relinquish control over my anger. I was unwilling to become angry or to openly admit angry feelings. Even on 7-B, I needed to be liked by all. I wanted approval and, of course, understanding. I even expected a little sympathy because of my pain and because of my all-out effort to overcome it. The whole time, of course, I kept a stiff upper lip and showed no anger, only determination. I had backed myself into a corner that was terribly difficult to get out of.

But I had to consider what Dr. Covington had told me about anger. He could help me. He seemed to have no doubt that there was something more for me than pain for the rest of my life. He said he could help because I was willing to talk. Was I? Was I willing to put myself down even farther by giving in to his suggestion that indeed I was an angry person? Was it the unconscious anger I harbored that was making my pain worse? Did I really believe that? Or was I becoming so confused that I no longer knew the difference between what my real feelings were and what thoughts were being driven into my head by Dr. Covington and the rest of the staff? It was, at the moment, more than I was willing to admit, but they did start me thinking. Indeed, they started me thinking more than I wanted to.

I realized that there might be more to me than I was able to understand. Such thoughts made me feel alone and frightened, and I wanted to run away, but I knew that I couldn't. No matter where I went, my own thoughts would still be with me. I knew it would be impossible to empty my mind or to wipe out all the past events in my life that had helped shape and mold me into what I was. Running was not the answer. Like it or not, I knew I would have to begin searching for answers that would help me, as Dr. Covington put it, "Get in touch with your feelings so that you can begin to deal with them and help yourself to a less painful life." I did not want the staff to change me. I merely wanted to remain who I was and just get rid of the pain. But I was beginning to realize that I might have to put all my cards on the table and pick them back up in another order.

On the Thursday before, Stella had given each of us a copy of *The Angry Book*. I now picked it up and slowly thumbed through the first few pages, which I had already attempted to read before. None of what I had read that day stayed with me. It was as if I had never read a single word; not even the chapter headings were familiar. I recognized that this was probably because the book was threatening to me. It could prove that everyone at the Clinic was right, that I was angry. I knew that speculation would not solve anything, but reading might, so I began.

I was fighting mixed feelings as I began to read. The author's style was simple and easy to follow. His points were clear, no double meanings. He mentioned a secret pact with yourself in which you tell yourself that no matter what, you won't get angry. He suggested that those of us who promise ourselves not to allow anger to dominate our emotions are really looking for love, understanding, and compassion. None of these can be obtained by ugly, angry people.

God, that hit me hard! It was as if he had written that just for me, as if he knew that I allowed my need for love and acceptance control my expressions of anger. My low self-esteem gave me a great need for love. Since I couldn't love myself, I looked to others for love, hoping that their admiration for my willingness to comply with almost any request would build up my self-esteem a little.

Dr. Theodore Rubin, the author, wrote about people who must stay in control because of their fear of anger. I thought, that must be the control everyone around here is telling me I have. The author also wrote that for these people, everything must be predicted before it happens, thus giving them control over any situation. Is that why I run when a situation becomes unpredictable, uncontrollable?

The book talked about a slush fund of anger in which all us "nice people" store our angry feelings. It allows us to hide our anger in a safe place so no one can see it. The only trouble is that after a while it gets pretty damn heavy carrying all that anger around. I asked myself, could the anger become painful enough to feel physically? My pain—did I do this to myself? Did I create the pain in my body by ignoring angry feelings, keeping my true feelings hidden from even myself? Is it my fault I am hurting so much?

Putting anger into different categories made it almost too easy. As I read each page, words jumped out at me. "Guilt," "Denial," "Don't worry about me," "Always tired," "I'm with you." The list went on and on. Each one of these chapters pointed out situations that applied to me. They revealed feelings I had denied.

I began the chapter "Putting It Off." Dr. Rubin spoke of people who do not get angry, but rather put off or suppress their anger until another time. By putting off such anger they build up a slush fund of anger that does not go away, but grows until something, big or small, appropriate or not, triggers it off. They react by getting angry with someone like themselves who puts off the anger until another poor victim comes along to get victimized by a put-offer.

That was me! I was a put-off person. I was the kind of person who, when faced with a situation that should have made me angry, would fail to come up with the right argument and would say nothing until I was with someone safe and began to think the situation over. Then I got angry. Unfortunately, Scott was usually that person. He was my safe person. For reasons not yet known to me at that point in my stay, I felt secure with Scott. He allowed me to express anger in front of him. For all I knew, he might have been a put-off person too. I was not sure. The point was that I did have anger, and it came out with Scott.

I was always a good one for saying, "I should have said." After the fact, I could come up with just the right comeback, the perfect comment to avoid being put down by someone else. I knew that such behavior made me angry. By the time I finished reading the book, I knew I had a lot of anger inside of me. I was not the nice, congenial person I thought I was. But instead of taking the book at face value, I read all sorts of things into it. I saw myself as a very angry, unfeeling person. I felt that I had used and abused people all my life. Once again I managed to find the worst in myself and hold on to it.

I finished the book that evening. I had been drawn to it, its words, its accusations, and its analysis of the logic of anger. But I could feel myself withdrawing further as I misinterpreted what the book said. When I put the book down, my mind closed to all outside sounds as I leaped into deep thought, unaware of my surroundings; I went into an almost trancelike state. Time was irrelevant as I sat there in the darkened room, the sunlight long since gone, only the hall light creating a cold gray glow in the otherwise empty room. It wasn't until Suzy returned from her evening visit with Sam that her squeaky voice brought me back to reality. What ever it was I had been focusing on so intently vanished from my mind. No thoughts, feelings, or real memory of what I had read remained, only a sense of annoyance with Suzy for returning.

NOVEMBER 6, TUESDAY

The lounge was dingy, in spite of the large picture window opposite the door. The musty smell of smoke, coffee, and half eaten fruit choked the air. Group was ready to begin. "My wife messed up my life something awful. First she took the kids away from me when I got sick. She couldn't take my sickness. She up and went home to her mother. I thought for sure she would come back to me. After all, she was my wife, and my little boys meant everything to me." Jim sat across the room wringing his hands, his arms and hands in constant motion as if all his feelings were working their way down to his finger tips. By twisting his hands, he could finally get rid of the painful memories. His voice became softer, his pain and disappointment filling his voice "When my wife was in that car accident, she was killed you know . . ." He stopped a moment, lost in thought, his eyes fixed on the dull green carpet covering the floor. He seemed to be thinking of the accident. His tight jaw and clenched teeth showed the anger he felt inside.

"Well, my mother-in-law had a judge order me to never again come near them boys. I still can't believe that judge would do something like that. My mother-in-law told the judge I was on drugs and drank so much I never sobered up. The fool judge believed her, and I ain't seen them boys since." Jim's eyes were still fixed on the floor, his body still rigid and tense. The indignation and sorrow was visible on his face.

Moments passed while Jim sat quietly. No one felt able to relieve his pain with words. Suddenly Jim raised his head and with a complete change in tone—hopeful, alive, a sense of promise in his voice-he said, "Now, my second wife, she's different. Her kids is more like me own. They care 'bout me. I'm a daddy to them. They don't have some old fool woman puttin' all kind of things in their head about me that just ain't true. I have a new life now with Roberta and her three kids." But Jim's head hung low as he finished his story. His old wounds were still unhealed. They could not be forgotten so easily.

It was like coming into the middle of a sad movie as Jim shared with us the grief and heartache his pain had caused. For the first time I saw his human side. He allowed his feelings to be expressed openly and frankly as we sat quietly listening to him unfold his life's turbulent narrative.

Jim's need to understand his heartache better allowed him to add, "I was only married to her for four years. We had three little boys, one right after the next. I thought we were happy, I really did. She never complained to me. I worked hard to provide for her and the kids." A puzzled look came onto Jim's face. He was clearly having trouble remaining in control of his emotions, and an angry look came over his face. His eyes narrowed and deep frown lines appeared on his forehead. "I was hurt on the job. Hell, I was just tryin' to make a decent livin' for 'em. Not one damn doctor could find the trouble. First there was all those operations. Then the doctors kep' a pushin' these damn pills at me. I had no choice but to take 'em, I was hurtin' like a son of a bitch! My wife made sure I took 'em." His fist pounded his thigh, but he seemed unaware of his actions.

Jim suddenly stopped pounding his leg, his voice trailing off, no sound, no expression. A deflated man, only remotely aware of his surroundings he sat hunched in the old, faded chair in the corner of the lounge. I could feel my own pain build as I listened to his story. I too knew what emotional pain was like. I knew the same kind of hurt and disappointment. I too felt that if you can no longer perform for others and be of some use to them, they will cast you aside like an old shoe. My usefulness had come to an end the day my pain gained control of me and I felt my purpose in life was over. Each of us sat quietly in the lounge, lost in our own sadness.

My thoughts quickly called up an incident with my mother several years before. I stood in my kitchen, leaning against the counter. There was a slight breeze working its way across the dinning room into the kitchen from the open door. Summer was coming to an end. I had summoned my mother. I had to talk with her. It had been almost eighteen months since we'd last spoken to each other.

My mind was trying desperately to find the right words to begin the conversation. What does one say to one's own mother after eighteen months of silence? I felt the hurt in my heart as I wondered to myself, "Why didn't she try to talk to me? What made her stay away so long? Didn't she care? How could she live with herself?"

"I guess you wondered why I called you after such a long time?"

"Yes, I did." she replied in a matter-of-fact tone.

I could not look at her. My eyes were beginning to water, and I didn't want her to see. "I really tried to tell myself that it didn't matter whether or not you ever spoke to me again. I thought I could live with it. But . . . I can't. I cannot deal with the thoughts inside my head. Every time I think about you, my own mother, at such a distance, my heart sinks. Every time the kids ask what's happened to Grandma, my stomach does flip-flops. As time went by I even had trouble remembering why we were not talking. All I know is that I cannot live like this. I can't live with myself knowing that you or Dad might never get to see the kids again. That something could happen to you." Now the tears were running down my face as the words came spilling out. "I just cannot deal with the situation. I have to try to remedy it."

I stopped to look at my mother, to see if she was hearing what I said, to see if she was feeling what I said. I was hoping that she was as filled with remorse as I. But I still sensed the distance, the indifference of her—no sign in her face that would indicate to me that she felt as I did.

"Well, Penney, you know your father and I have always tried to do everything we could for you. We have always given you whatever we could. We did not understand why you ceased to communicate with us." She paused for a moment. "We talked about it a lot and decided that when you were ready to talk to us again, you would come to us. Time was on our side.''

I'm sorry . . . I don't know what got into me. I guess I was just feeling tired. I just couldn't . . .'' I stopped. There was no way I could explain to her that the demands placed on me at that moment were beyond my physical endurance. I did not look sick, now or then. I assumed that she felt my refusal to continue as we had been was a personal affront. She would never understand that I was physically unable to keep up with all the demands made on me. I could no longer perform for them. And with that came a sudden rejection from her, unfair and unfounded. So, there I stood. I was apologizing to my own mother for being who I was, less than perfect, less than completely willing to drop everything each time I was asked. And, I sensed that was just the kind of apology my mother felt she deserved.

The rest of the time I spent with her that day was very difficult. I could not look her in the eye. I had done what I had to in order to live with myself, but I had once again transformed my personality to suit their needs. I suppressed my anger, realizing there was no way my mother would tell me she was sorry for allowing this silence to go on so long. She felt no remorse whatsoever, or at least she did not show it.

My mother left that day with my promise that I would try to reinstate our relationship; I would try to mend my ways and be exactly what they wanted.

As the curtain fell on the memory in my mind, I thought about what Jim had said; he could not see his kids. Yes, he could have, if he really cared enough. But, he didn't. My mother, if she had truly cared, would have made some attempt to communicate with me. I knew that if I had been in her position, with my children, I would be knocking down their door until we resolved the problem. No amount of anger is worth the loss of a child or a mother. But I had lost my mother for over a year because of angry words. And now I realized she did not even care enough to try to understand, to work out the problem. It was not until I called her and apologized for being me that our relationship was slowly, over time, restored.

"Jim? Jim! How do you feel about all that?" Dr. Covington asked, breaking the somber mood.

Jim sighed as he said, "I just want to see my boys 'gain. I ain't seen them since my wife died. They're my kids, too. Right?" a hopeful look in his eye, anticipating an affirmative answer.

But, you have to try. They won't come to you. If it's important enough, you'll find a way.

Without directly answering Jim's question, Dr. Covington repeated his question louder. "How do you feel about it? What kind of feelings do you experience when you think about it?"

Jim's expression changed quickly. His eyes became alive and intense, his body straight and stiff, as he answered quickly, "Mad as hell. I know I have every right to see those kids and I'm gonna do just that when I leave here! I know I can handle it now! You've helped me a lot to understand all that stuff." Jim pointed his finger at Dr. Covington as he spoke. "My limp ain't as bad as when I got here. I know now that I don't need any more surgery to fix me up. Four was four too many. I am who I am, and I do believe I can find my boys and at least let them know I'm still alive. Maybe I can even get 'em to come and stay with me this summer and help out on the farm. Farm never was a money-maker, but it helps. Boys should like that," Jim said with determination in his voice.

Stella, who had remained quiet through most of the group, spoke in an encouraging tone. "I think you have done some good work on your feelings. Just remember, Jim, you are the one who has control, not your pain. Don't allow your own self-doubts to interfere with rational judgment on your part."

"I ain't ever gonna get messed up with pills and booze again. That stuff would have killed me eventually. No more for me. Now it's just me and the missus and her kids. And maybe—if it's to be—my sons. I can live with that. I think I can live with that,'' he said, trying to reinforce his belief in himself.

"I think you can, Jim," Dr. Covington said optimistically.

"Yeah, I think I gots it all under control now. I'm ready to go home. End of the week, Doc?" Jim asked hopefully.

Dr. Covington did not acknowledge the question. He returned the conversation to Jim's anger. "What about controlling your anger. Can you keep your temper in control? Will you be able to deal with each situation as it arises, or will you still let all this crap build up inside of you?

"Well, I feel good that I can understand that some folks make me angry, my mother-in-law for one, but that's okay. Findn' my boys is more important than that old woman. You taught me to recognize what's important. I think I can begin to get my needs taken care of first. I can't save the world, Doc." Jim smiled, an air of confidence in his expression. He had gained a great deal of understanding about himself during his stay here. I just prayed I would be half as successful as he.

I never really got to know Jim until that day. I had only been in the Clinic for a week, and most of that time I had spent with Suzy. That group meeting was really the first time Jim had shared his thoughts. He had been on 7-B almost four weeks, but a lot of that time he had not attended group—there had been none because he had been the only pain patient and had talked with Dr. Covington one-on-one or with the staff nurses.

In the days that followed, Jim and I walked down to the cafeteria together for dinner. It wasn't until he had opened up in group that he really began to talk during dinner. Before that we had just sat and occasionally commented on the weather or the poor quality of the food. Suddenly he seemed to have a need to tell me how he felt about 7-B and Dr. Covington. He encouraged me to open up as much as I could with Dr. Covington.

"Even though it don't make sense right now," Jim explained, "you got to tell them what you feel. It sort of all comes together at some point and you feel different, free. I mean it's like you finally understand who you are, what you want. That you're just as good as those other folks out there." I didn't understand what he was telling me at the time. I still had a very long way to go.

Jim's determination to leave the Clinic became more apparent as each day passed. He admitted to me that before he came to the Clinic he had not only had a drug problem but had been chasing down his Percodan and Valium with a beer every time he took one. Now with his dependency under control and a better understanding of himself, thanks to Dr. Covington, he was ready to leave.

NOVEMBER 7, WEDNESDAY

I was feeling insignificant and somewhat guilty as I walked into group that morning. I was not sure if my presence on the unit was justified. As I entered the room I was greeted by a stranger, a woman in her mid-forties, overweight, and looking very frightened. What was so different about her? She was in a wheelchair. Helplessly, she sat in the middle of the room. Suzy entered the room and saw the wheelchair. She responded with a simple, "Oh!"

"Good morning, Penney and Suzy. We have a new member with us this morning. I'll wait till Jim gets here to introduce her. Where is Jim, anyway? He's late." Stella walked over to her usual position behind the video camera, forgetting that it was broken. Dr. Covington will be here in a minute, he's writing some orders at the nurses station.

"Sorry, gang." Dr. Covington apologized. "Where's Jim? He should be here. He isn't out of here until Friday." Dr. Covington quickly picked up the phone on the empty desk in front of him and dialed. He was irritated that he had to make the call. "Sue, see if Jim is in his room and tell him to get his buns over here right now!" He hung up the phone and remarked, "I hate to have to wait for people," forgetting that we had been waiting for him.

Dr. Covington settled back into his chair as he always did, saying in his therapeutic tone, "Have you two been introduced to Carol? She's going to join your pain group." He seemed pleased that there was still another member to our rather small group of three unresponsive people.

"Why don't you begin, Carol. Tell us a little bit about how you managed to end up here on the pain unit." Dr. Covington said mildly.

"Well . . ." The voice that came from the overweight blond woman in the chair was hoarse, yet timid and cautious. "I was transferred over here from the main hospital. I came in for my back; I've had three disks removed. The doctor told me he couldn't do any more for me. Surgery would only make my pain worse." She stopped for a minute, her eyes, behind thick glasses appeared magnified as she stared blankly into space. "He said . . . I would never walk again." Tears ran down her checks and she quickly wiped them away with her hand. Carol looked to Dr. Covington as if to say, "Please, don't make me do this," but she got no help.

Her composure now slightly restored, she continued. "Dr. Covington came to see me a couple of days ago. He told me I *could* walk again and that there *was* something I could do to get back on my feet. I don't know." Once again the tears took control of her.

"What I said is that it's possible that if you really work at it, you might be able to walk again. We don't perform miracles here. You have to work for what you get." Dr. Covington corrected her with a gentle note in his voice.

Pushing her short bangs out of her face, Carol said hopefully, "I'm willing to try. You said you can help me, and I'm going to hold you to that."

My mind began flooding with questions as I listened to the exchange between Carol and Dr. Covington. Why had Dr.

Covington put her in a program that would be impossible for her? What did they want from her? She was trapped, and I could sense how she felt—embarrassed and very much alone.

Dr. Covington asked Carol to tell the group something about herself. Carol willingly began. "I live with my three children and one of my brothers. I lost my husband ten years ago. He was a good man, but God took him away from me." Once again she burst into tears. Her words were difficult to understand, but she continued haltingly in spite of the tears. "All I really want from life is to be able to take care of myself, my kids, and feel good." She stopped and buried her face in the sleeve of her robe, unable to control herself any longer.

Stella walked over to her and pulled several tissues out of her jacket pocket. "I always come prepared. Tears are a part of this group," she joked. "It's okay."

Carol took a minute to regain control and said in a tone filled with doubt and fear, "I don't know if I belong here. I don't know if I belong anywhere. I have taken care of people all my life, but where are they when you need them? Where are they!" Her tone turning harsh and resentful.

For the next forty minutes the group focused on the issue Carol had brought up: Where are the people when you need them? Why do people avoid someone who is not "normal?" I had asked myself those questions many times, but I was never sure what the answers were. I sat quietly, listening to Carol explain how on numerous occasions she had put her own needs second so that she could help someone else out. "All my life I felt obligated to help out my brothers and sisters. Our mother was dead, our father was unwilling to take care of us, so I took on the role of mother at the age of thirteen. And . . ." Carol's voice now rose several decibels, her strong negative feelings toward her brothers and sisters surfacing as she said, "when I really needed them, when I needed their support and help during my husband's death and after several of my operations, where were they? Now my brother is living with me again because he had some financial problems. I didn't turn my back on him. Why? Why?'' Carol again broke down and cried uncontrollably.

My body had become tense as I sat listening to Carol pour her heart out to the group. I had had those same feelings toward people in my life, my mother included, though I would never openly admit to them in group. While I didn't want attention because I was unable to function, I did want understanding, understanding that I believed was not available to me. Group provided me with many opportunities to reexamine feelings I had denied. Carol's reaction to her family's indifference sparked my resentment. My heart went out to her as she sat helpless in her steel chair, unable to fight back.

Dr. Covington ended group that morning with the statement, ''I heard a lot of feelings being shared in here today. I believe we have the makings of a very good group here. Good work, turkeys!'' As he reached the door to leave, he turned around and, directing his words to Stella, said, ''Find out why Jim didn't show up this morning. He isn't out of here yet!''

The room emptied in a matter of seconds. Stella wheeled Carol out the door, and Suzy headed to her room to prepare for still another test. I sat alone. A cloud-filled sky hung outside the window. I thought about Carol. I felt sorry for her. She was starting out with two strikes against her already. She knew what her situation was, and no amount of reassurance from Dr. Covington was going to help her believe she would ever walk again. All she wanted to do was to be able to take care of herself. She wasn't asking for much, but what she was asking for might not be within her reach.

NOVEMBER 8, THURSDAY

Carol sat once again in the middle of the room as she spun out the story of her life. She seemed slightly more at ease on the second day. Perhaps spending one night in the psych ward was somehow reassuring, if one managed to get a good night's sleep. Whatever the reason, Carol was quite open about herself as she calmly explained, "My husband died ten years ago, right before my back trouble started. He was the best thing that ever happened to me in my life, and he was taken away from me. I loved that man! I tried the best I could to take care of the kids, to be both a mother and father to them and to give them all I could."

She smiled as she spoke of her children. "I have three kids, two boys and a girl. It was difficult to raise those kids on my own, even though my husband left me some money. I was physically unable to keep up with them after my back problem started. I am willing to go it alone, but I need to be healthy to do that. I even went back to school so I could get a better job to give my kids everything."

Her eyes, hidden behind her glasses, peered at me as she spoke. "We were raised in a home for children. My mother died when I was thirteen. I was the first to leave the home and get a job. Little by little, I managed to get each of my brothers and sisters out of the home, and I took care of them. I found them jobs to help them become more independent. I even managed to help one sister get into college. I was working two jobs at that point to help with expenses. They all depended on me. Once I was unable to help them any longer, when I needed their help, they were nowhere to be found." Her voice now trailed off to a soft whisper as her mind recaptured her youth.

Breaking the silence in the room, Dr. Covington turned to look directly at me as if to read my mind, then asked, as if he already knew the answer, "Penney, can you relate to what Carol is saying? Any feelings about it?"

I thought for a moment, unable to meet his eyes, staring at the scuffed gray floor before I said, "I don't know. I wasn't raised in a children's home. What do you mean?" I turned my attention toward him, waiting for an answer.

"You know what I mean. Being used by other people, then when you are no longer able to serve them, they turn away from you. Don't you feel anything when you hear Carol?'' His eyes were fixed on me in anticipation of my answer.

Nervous that I would say the wrong thing, I said, ''I feel bad for her. A lot of people are like that. They will only stick around if you can do something for them.'' I could hear the anger in my own voice.

''You do feel something then, don't you?'' he asked, sure of himself.

''Yes.'' It's sad people have to be so unwilling, so unfeeling, so . . .''

Interpreting the exchange between Dr. Covington and myself, Carol added, ''I am angry at all my brothers and sisters. After all I did for them, they turned their backs on me. And now . . . the hell with them!'' Anger raged in Carol as she suddenly realized that she was alone now. ''I am going to get better! I'll be damned if they'll get away with this! I'm going to get better and have one hell of a life without them! Just me and my kids!'' Like a chameleon, Carol changed completely right before our eyes. She went from being a timid, insecure child-woman to a determined, outgoing person who finally knew what she wanted. It was hard for me to believe that she could transform herself so quickly, but as the days went by, I saw this again and again.

I was still having a great deal of difficulty relating to Stella. Instead of hearing her genuine concern for me, I heard her telling me how I *should* feel and act. It felt as if my parents were in the room when Stella talked. I had never been allowed to think for myself, at least that is what I believed. I was so easily controlled as a child. Why was I always being corrected for being like a child, when I *was* a child! Manners were very important to my parents, and I tried my best to follow their instructions. Every time I stepped out of line I was corrected. I can still remember being made to feel as if I had hurt them personally, and the remorse I felt as I vowed never to ''offend'' them again. By the time I was in my teens, their words were deeply embedded in my mind, and there was little I dared do to oppose them.

Now, here was Stella trying to shape me into what she felt would be best for everyone. At least that's the way I saw her attempt to force me to make decisions. She rarely gave me a chance to express my feelings, but then I never tried to.

One of Stella's chief topics was about my setting priorities. (The most she ever talked to Suzy about was washing her hair, which she had still not done well into the second week of my stay.) ''Have to set those priorities!'' she kept repeating, but whose priorities was she talking about?

Joan, on the other hand, seemed to be willing to listen to me when I chose to tell her how I was really feeling. Quite often, however, I would say nothing about my feelings to Joan during our long talks because I was afraid I would, by expressing my true feelings, alienate her, and I could not chance that. I needed her compassion and understanding.

Stella and Joan both had the same objective, but they went about it in different ways. I was more receptive to Joan, I trusted her more. Both of them encouraged me to rework my priorities and begin to put myself at the top of my list, to recognize how important it was for me to like myself. I should be the one to decide how to feel and act, and not allow others' personal judgment control me. I should be who I am by my own choice, and not because someone else wants me to conform to his or her idea of who I am.

During the previous year or so I had let pain dominate my life. I had forgotten what was important to me and put myself down as a lost cause. Joan picked up on this right away. She saw my deep self-doubt and was willing to spend the time to help me rebuild my self-image. I didn't realize then that unless I felt good about myself, my efforts to overcome the pain would be in vain. I needed to believe that I was strong enough to get better for myself. That is where Joan started. She knew how important my children and husband were to me and took that as a starting point.

"You know, unless you begin to believe in yourself a little more, your attitude will eventually show through to your children and they will begin to get a distorted view of both you and themselves." I doubted what Joan said, but I listened as we sat together in my room.

"I should be home right now with the kids and Scott instead of taking so much time here for myself," I said. I was still feeling guilty about taking the time to get things clear in my mind. I also didn't believe I was worthy of the time and effort given to me on 7-B. "If it hadn't been for the pain, I could have been a better mother to them." Now feeling sad, recalling moments spent with my children, I said, "I can't even hold Scotty or allow him to get too close to me. Do you know what that does to me? I'm worthless to them . . ." I didn't want to express the rest of my thought—that they'd be better off if I didn't return home.

"You are their mother and they need you, regardless of your physical condition. If they are the most important thing in your life, then begin to find ways to express that to them. If you can like yourself, take some well-deserved time to sort out a few issues. I believe wholeheartedly that you can be the kind of mother you want to be." By the concern in Joan's eyes, I could see her words were sincere. She looked directly at me. "You have a long way to go, but we are all going to do it together. Right?"

"Yeah," I said, but I was still not sure I'd be able to change who I was.

As Joan left my room that evening, I momentarily believed it was possible for me to like myself. Never before had my life been so centered around myself. Now, for the first time, people were telling me to think about my own needs above everything else. Even though I was removed both physically and emotionally from Pittsburgh, I still felt I should think of my kids first. Isn't that what everyone would expect me to do? How could I put them aside, even for a little while. Yet it was happening! I was not really missing them. They were out of my sight, and regrettably, they were being pushed out of my mind. I was becoming wrapped up in myself, and the guilt was tearing me apart.

Later that evening David came to my room, his red hair looking much softer in the pale evening light. My first encounter with David on Halloween had been awkward for me. He had been the one who ended up on the floor while two women tickled him. I must admit I was afraid of him at first. He was not one of the pain patients; he was a psych patient. David was no more than twenty years old, and he seemed so innocent, so naive about life.

"You busy, Penney?" he asked, his voice breaking the silence.

"No, not really." I looked up at him. He looked sad.

"Can I come in for a minute? I just want to talk. Do you mind?" he asked in an apologetic voice.

I had always possessed a mothering instinct. I don't think I realized it at the time, but David fulfilled a small part of me that needed to mother someone, and he was in need of someone who would not try to analyze his every word. We satisfied each other's needs.

"What's wrong? You don't look very happy," I said as he entered my room.

"I just talked to my mom. She doesn't understand. I don't know how I can make her understand me."

"What doesn't she understand?" I had no idea why David was on the psych ward. That was one thing that was never asked. A few patients were willing to volunteer such information, almost proud of being a problem to society. David was not one of those: he remained very private.

"Oh . . ." His voice began to quiver. "She wants me to be home by the end of next week. She says I have had long enough to get my act together. She doesn't understand. I am supposed to finish college, a major that she picked for me. I hate engineering! But she won't listen to me. And there is this girl, Mary Beth. Mary Beth is nice and all, but I don't love her. But until I can tell my mother that I will marry Mary Beth and finish school, she won't be happy.''

David fell silent for a few moments, as he paced back and forth in front of me. ''God! What the hell am I going to do? I want to . . . to . . .''

''You sound like you're afraid.''

''I am. The problem is, I'm not sure why.''

I was feeling far too uncertain of my own destiny to be able to give him any kind of direction. All I could do was listen. I wanted to reassure him, let him know that everything would be okay. But I didn't. ''David . . .''

''What?''

''No one knows where they're going. I thought I had my life all in order, and look where I am now. I'm not sure of what I want either. All I know is that this place is the last stop for me. I can work with them or I can ignore what they say and leave here in the same shape I came in.'' I paused a moment, not knowing what to say. I was just as confused as David.

''Penney.''

''What?''

''Do you think I am a loser?''

''No! At least you are here trying to help yourself. You are trying. That is all any of us can do—try.''

''They keep telling me here that I have to be the one to make up my mind. They say that I can't live for my mother. I have to live for me. That is so hard. I have spent my entire life doing what other people tell me. I thought I was making progress—until I talked to Mom. She seems to suffocate me with every word she speaks. My chest gets tight, I can hardly get my breath. I actually have passed out in midsentence just talking to her. I won't bore you with all the details of my sordid relationship with my mother. If only my dad were still alive . . . then things would be . . .''

I was very much like David. All he really wanted was to please his mother. Now he realized that he had needs of his own. His mind and heart were being torn between his needs and his mother's. I too had realized that I had personal needs I had never acknowledged. Recognizing them was the easy part. Now both David and I would have to learn how to fulfill our own needs and still be able to live with the people in our lives.

"Sometimes I wish . . ." He stopped.

"Wish what?"

His eyes closed, his head dropped as he let out a deep sigh.

"What, David?"

The silence seemed to go on for a long time before he answered. "Nothing. Nothing at all. I better get back to my room. I have some letters to write." He got up from the chair and walked toward the door. "Thanks for listening. I'll catch to you later," and he was gone.

NOVEMBER 9, FRIDAY MORNING

My God! She's dead! I killed her! The gun had let out one loud bang as the bullet left the chamber and entered her skull, draining every ounce of life from the body in front of me. Her face was colorless. Her large brown eyes were fixed directly on me as I stood before her. Her arms hung lifelessly down the sides of the chair, her fingertips barely reaching the floor. The stain grew larger on the rug as her life slowly drained down her arm. Her head was rigid, her mouth gaped open, an expression of horror on her white face. She had not expected her life to come to such a sudden and violent end.

Run! Run! Keep breathing . . . Run . . .

"Penney. Time to get up." Stella's low, harsh voice broke the dreadful visions going through my mind.

I was afraid to open my eyes. I felt certain that when I did, there would be a grotesque figure, eyes fixed hauntingly on me, the blood still oozing from the side of her skull. I imagined her hair all matted and dripping with the thick red substance. The vision had been much too real. I could still hear the explosion of the gun ringing in the stillness of the night, but I could not remember why it had happened. Only the terror remained.

The fear of even thinking such a terrible thing clung to me as I slowly opened my eyes. Turning my head, I forced myself to look toward the chair near the window. I felt tremendous relief as I saw that it was empty. It had been only a dream, but such violent dreams, so uncaring of human life, were completely foreign to me. The image of Lori, my sister-in-law, robbed of a future in a momentary act of violence, haunted me as I slowly got out of bed. Of all the dreams in the world to remember! I must have had many good dreams in my lifetime, why did this one have to linger in my thoughts?

Carol was a member of our group only for the two hours every morning when we gathered in the lounge or across the hall to "get in touch with our feelings." It had been difficult for me to deal with Carol during group. Her lack of mobility scared me. My first encounter with her, sitting abandoned in the middle of the room, unable to defend herself physically or emotionally, struck a nerve. During my long struggle with pain, I often feared becoming like Carol, unable to take care of myself and depending on those around me for my simplest needs. Because her presence reinforced that fear, I chose to keep her at arm's length. I not only thought that I could not help her, but she created a great deal of fear and anger in me.

Before being transferred to 7-B, Carol had received a nerve block, which the doctors hoped would reduce the leg pain caused by the scarring from several back operations. The procedure is simple: Once the physician has determined which nerves are sending pain messages to the brain, he can treat these nerves. By injecting carefully measured doses of drugs into predetermined areas, it is possible to completely eliminate the pain for up to six months. Patients can gradually increase activities and resume much of their normal life.

Friday morning, as I sat in my usual seat waiting for the others to arrive, I got the shock of my life. Carol walked into

group on her own! She was slow and awkward, supporting her
weight on an old, green, straight-back chair that she pushed
in front of her, but she was supporting most of her weight
with her legs. It was a miracle! Her nerve block had been successful. Only two days before, Stella had pushed this frightened
woman into group, helpless and very much alone. Now she
seemed no longer frightened. She was radiant. Her eyes,
though still hidden by her glasses, managed to glow from
behind them. Her expression reflected the immense sense of
accomplishment she felt as she slowly pushed the chair in front
of her and made her way to a place in the circle.

Group that morning was completely centered around Carol.
We talked not only about the fact that she could use her legs
but about all the anger she had toward the many doctors who
were positive she would never walk again. "The first thing
I am going to do when I get home is go tell that son of a bitch
exactly what I think of him. He would have allowed me to
remain in the damn chair the rest of my life." Carol's voice
was no longer timid or shy. 'I can't imagine how they could
have done that to me! Why would they do it?'' The perplexing question was repeated several times as Carol tried to understand why she had been so misled.

"I know exactly how you feel Carol!" Suzy said. "I've been
to some of those doctors who don't have the brains God gave
them! They don't care how much you hurt. All they want to
do is get you out of their office. Believe me I know!"

"I just can't believe I might have spent the rest of my damn
life in a wheelchair! God it's so unreal!"

"You know, people with chronic pain usually accept what
the doctor tells them without questioning. They are given
medication and told to stop certain activities. You usually avoid
questioning the medical profession rather than have them think
you are questioning their motives. That leads to many unanswered questions, self-doubt mostly about your pain—and
more stress for you and your family. What really happens is
that the doc gets tired of you coming back time after time,
still complaining of the same pain. He is more than willing

to give you another script just to silence you. You take the pills, don't get better, and start your downhill slide. You guys are going to have to learn to communicate with your docs.'' Dr. Covington always referred to doctors as docs. ''Find out why you are taking the medication, what it will do for you, and what the side effects are. You have a right to that information, and quite often the doctor will think more of you. By being a 'people pleaser' you communicate the message that you really don't care and are expecting your doctor to take full responsibility for your recovery. You have to show them that you are willing to help yourself.''

As the group came to an end, I noticed that Carol's confidence, not only in her ability to walk but also in her ability to be a better person, grew rapidly. The nerve block had done its job. Carol was able to stand on her own two feet and face the world with a renewed sense of dignity.

Without hesitation, Carol followed me out of the room, still pushing her chair in front of her, and stood by the elevator. ''What are you going to do?'' I asked her.

''Why, I'm going to go down to sports medicine with you. No time like the present to get started.'' Carol seemed determined to make the very most of each second of life. ''I have spent the last six months of my life flat on my back. You don't think I'm about to go back to that room and sit any more. I'm going to go to sports medicine and work out!''

Jim was gone, Carol had taken her first steps, and even Suzy managed to get her hair washed during the course of the day. It was Friday, time to wind things up for another week and to think ahead to Saturday and being ''normal'' for two days. It was also time for Dr. Covington to talk with each of us privately about progress or problems that we might want to discuss. A time for openness and honesty!

In group that morning, although Carol's enthusiasm was the only issue we addressed, I had remained fairly quiet. Yet my dream still hung on the edge of my consciousness all day.

I had to talk with someone about it. I needed to be reassured that there was nothing wrong with me for having had that dream. Dr. Covington was the one I felt I could trust. As he entered my room, I prepared myself to try to explain the dream.

I could feel my body trembling as I looked at him, but his expression was so gentle and understanding that I started. I stammered, "I . . . I had a dream last night . . ."

"Oh. Want to tell me about it?"

"Yeah, that's why . . . I mentioned it. It's . . . difficult for me." I looked at him; his attention was focused on me, waiting for me to continue.

"Are you going to tell me about it?" Dr. Covington asked.

I continued, "I had this dream. It really scared me. I can't imagine why I would have dreamed it."

"Tell me what it was about." Dr. Covington was beginning to lose patience with my roundabout way of explaining.

"I . . . killed . . . someone in my dream." Looking at Dr. Covington as I spoke, I watched for some kind of reaction.

With an unchanged expression, he calmly asked, "Who did you kill?"

At first I was hesitant to share that part of my dream with him, but I had come that far, so I explained, "It was Lori, the girl Scott's brother married two years ago."

"What does she mean to you now? Are you close to her or are there some bad feelings between you two?" His voice still very calm.

It was his relaxed manner that allowed me to say, "There are quite a few bad feelings between us. I really don't care for her at all. But why would she come to haunt me here? What reason would I have to kill her?"

"What does she look like? Tall, short, fat, ugly?" A smile appeared on his face as he said "ugly."

"She is average looking, I guess. Dark hair, neatly dressed, but it is her voice, her insincere sweetness that drives me crazy. She is so self-centered. She is one of those people who honestly believes she can do no wrong." My voice became more agitated as I spoke of her.

"I don't really think it is her that you wanted to kill, but someone similar to her, either in dress, mannerisms, or attitude. Can you think of anyone who looks even a little bit like her or acts like her?"

I sat staring at the floor, my mind filled with images of people. I felt that Dr. Covington already knew who I was thinking of. One face kept coming back to me. A face that I knew only too well. My mother! She could, when it suited her, be as sweet and insincere as anyone. I sometimes had trouble believing what she said because I had too often heard her say things I knew she did not mean. She could tell people one thing and then turn right around and say something else when talking with someone else. I didn't trust Lori as far as I could throw her, and now, to my dismay, I realized my own mother was a great deal like Lori. I hated the thought of it. I hated myself as I looked at Dr. Covington and said, "My mother."

Once again, without any reaction, Dr. Covington said, "Sometimes it is easier for our minds to transfer negative feelings for one person onto someone else, someone less risky emotionally, less apt to become involved in present day life. You know, sometimes people get confused along the way. They feel that it is wrong to have any kind of negative feelings for someone they love. Love and hate are often misleading. You must admit you love Scott."

"Right," I said, not quite sure what he was getting at.

"But I bet there are times when you get pissed off with him."

"Right."

"I love my little boy, but there are times when I would like to wring his neck. That doesn't mean I don't love the little munchkin." Dr. Covington paused, shifting his weight in the chair. "It is impossible to go through life believing anger is wrong. No wonder you are so screwed up," he said with a smile on his face. "Why are you so afraid of becoming angry?

Are you willing to let people dump on you for the rest of your life?''

"No!" I almost shouted. I was angry at Dr. Covington for being so blunt. Feeling guilty, I said, "But I don't want to hurt anyone. Even if I did get angry, people, especially my mother, would tell me, 'Don't be like that!' " Waiting a moment as the words "Don't be like that" echoed in my head, I looked at him and said, "I can't be like I want. Nobody ever likes the way I react to things. I am either being too loud, too unreasonable, too selfish, too opinionated, or too . . . too much like they don't want me to be. I have always been told how to feel!" Anger swelled in me as I realized what I had just said.

"Then why in hell do you allow these people—your mother, your father, all the people you come in contact with—to tell you how to act, to think, what to say? Don't you have a mind of your own?"

"Yes! I have a mind of my own. It's just that it doesn't get me anywhere if I speak my mind. I always feel guilty if I do." My voice was now calmer and more reserved. The situation with my mother several years earlier quickly went through my mind. I had spoken my mind then, and what did it get me? Total and complete rejection for eighteen long painful months. I had learned my lesson well: do as you are told, feel as others want you to feel, be what others want you to be . . . or else . . . they will desert you.

"I bet you can't even tell someone off right, can you?" He looked at me as if to challenge my ability to express anger.

"Yes I can." Uncomfortable with the way this conversation had gone, I added, "But I need a good reason to get angry. I can't turn my emotions on and off like a water faucet."

"I want you to do something for me. I want you to pretend your mother is right in the room with us. She is sitting right here, on the edge of your bed, looking you right in the eye. You have just told her how you feel about something, and she tells you not to be like that. Tell her off. Get angry at her.'' His eyes now filled with anticipation, expecting me to carry out his desire.

I looked at the empty hospital bed before me. No one was there. No one had told me anything. I could not create anger in myself the way he wanted. I thought for several minutes, looked blankly at the bed and said, ''I can be me, right?'' my tone anything but firm.

''Is that what you call telling someone off? My five-year-old son can do better than that.''

''I need a reason to get mad. There isn't anyone there. I can't pretend.''

Dr. Covington stood up, walked toward me, placed himself behind my chair, leaned forward, and said, ''I'll stand here and tell you what to say. I think I can come up with some pretty angry words. You just repeat them for me. And put some feeling into it; remember you are mad!''

Without hesitation he began to say, ''I think you are not being reasonable.''

I repeated, ''I think you are not being reasonable.''

From behind me came, ''I have a right to feel this way.''

''I have a right to feel this way.'' My voice echoing his words.

''I want you to leave me alone and _____ off!'' his words ringing in my ears.

''I want you to leave me alone and . . . and . . . I can't say that!''

''The hell you can't! Tell her to _____ off!'' his voice demanding, intimidating.

''No!''   ''

''*Yes. Say it now!*'' I could feel his presence behind me as I tried to block him out, but I knew I would have to comply to satisfy him.

Again I began the phrase, ''I want you to . . . I can't!''

''Say _____ off, now!''

It was Dr. Covington's persistence that created enough anger in me to say, ''_____ off!'' As the words came out of my mouth, I felt dirty and abusive. He had controlled me, frightened me into saying what he felt I should. I had not used my own assertiveness, my own free will. I had said his four-letter word, a word I had hated, just to get rid of him. What made me really angry was that he seemed to enjoy every minute of it.

Dr. Covington had won that battle. He had one point on his side. There was a long hard war ahead of us. I swore to myself that I would never allow him to get to me like that again. As he left the room I could sense his triumph. I felt beaten. In the exchange of words that afternoon, he did manage to distract my thoughts from the dream. My mind was now filled with other worries.

NOVEMBER 9, FRIDAY EVENING

"All I have to do is think of it like going off to college and living in the dorm. That is what my daughter told me, just think of it as going off to college." Her eyes filled with enthusiasm and anticipation. Joyce, a small woman in her fifties with silver gray hair, seemed to have no reservations about being on the psych floor. She had somehow convinced herself that 7-B was nothing more than a natural place to be in her situation, a health club of sorts. Carol asked, "Doesn't it bother you, knowing the door is locked and everyone is watching your every move? They keep the door locked! Doesn't that bother you . . . to be locked up?" Her voice was louder than she had wanted.

I had gone to Carol's room to meet her new roommate. Carol's tried unsuccessfully to describe to Joyce the affect that the pain unit had on us. She had been concerned by Joyce's nonchalant attitude about being there. I thought to myself, She really doesn't understand, but she'll soon find out this place may well be the most difficult experience she has ever encountered. There was no way for me to explain this place to Joyce, so I decided to let her find out on her own. Soon enough reality would hit her-the locked door, the feeling of

being watched, the lack of personal freedom as we went about
our day like mechanical toys following a predetermined path.
I just hoped it would not hit her too hard.

"No! There is nothing wrong with being here! I know the
only reason is because I'm having trouble dealing with the
pain, not because I'm . . . crazy." Joyce now stopped, her
eyes, filled with hurt were fixed on Carol. "My daughter
cleared all that up for me. If Dr. Covington had his choice,
he would have his unit in another area of the Clinic altogether.
We don't need to be locked up. It's only because of the
crowded conditions that we have to be here. I'm not crazy;
I just have a problem with my mouth. It will be just like college, that's what my daughter said."

Joyce took a piece of fruit that her daughter had sent with
her, and began to eat it. It became apparent that her pain
was indeed in her face as she shifted the fruit from one side
of her mouth to the other while she tried to chew. She struggled
to open her mouth just wide enough to get a small bite.

NOVEMBER 10, SATURDAY

Dr. Gabis was now spending a great deal of time with me.
He had definite objectives in mind: he wished to guide me
gently into a better understanding of myself and my self-worth.
It was our talk the previous day that caused me to view my
relationship with Scott in a different light.

"You realize, don't you, that if you were as bad as you
have indicated, you would most likely still be alone in the
world. I seriously doubt that Scott, who seems to be very sen-
sible in his judgment, would be willing to spend the rest of
his life with someone who has nothing to offer. Don't you
think he is more selective than that? Would he have been willing to endure the emotional struggle of these past few years
with your situation if he did not truly love you? I don't think
so." His jaw tightened as he looked at me, waiting patiently
to hear my response.

"I don't know any more. I just feel so damn . . . so . . . worthless. I feel sorry for him because he's stuck with me and all my problems. He deserves better than that. You said it yourself, he is a truly nice guy. Maybe if . . ." My voice trailed off. My mind began to wonder.

If I gave him enough reason to turn his back on me, be distant enough so that he would no longer be willing to visit me, understand me, love me . . .

"You are going to have to be more realistic about yourself. You are the only one who doesn't believe in yourself. You can't live in your self-pity all your life. Everyone has good and bad qualities. You are no exception." Dr. Gabis's words "self-pity" rang in my head.

"No!" I was upset at his insinuation of self-pity. "Not self-pity, reality. Scott deserves better than me. If he got the chance, who knows, perhaps he would drift away from me. Perhaps in time he would see how much easier life would be without his crazy wife." A heaviness came over me as I fell silent.

It was that conversation with Dr. Gabis that helped me to distance myself from Scott. I began to slowly withdraw into myself in order to gain the insight I needed. I hoped that Scott would understand, or that he would not notice my emotional running away. I was going by a double standard: I was to be allowed to put distance between us but I expected Scott to stay close yet not notice. This sense of detachment grew, but it did not help me to become more objective. The guilt I felt about detaching from Scott would, in the end, play a big part in the day I almost lost myself.

NOVEMBER 11, SUNDAY

Sunday evening, I decided, would be the time I would regroup my thoughts, think about where I was and what I hoped to accomplish in the coming week. In the beginning, my one and only goal had been to get relief from my pain. I just wanted to feel better physically. That night, even taking into account that I had not done much for two days, my pain was less intense than usual, allowing me to think of other things, to focus on that glimmering light of freedom, the end of my stay in 7-B, and the steps I must take to reach it.

But I felt cold and alone facing the unknown obstacles that still stood in my way. I knew that I had not yet made an honest attempt to move toward that end. I always suppressed my feelings, convincing myself that they were either unimportant or impossible to deal with. Even what Dr. Gabis had said to me the previous day seemed unreal, distant.

I recalled a statement often made by both Dr. Covington and Stella: "There are some pain patients who have more reason to stay sick and remain patients than they have to take on the role of a well person." Is it possible that I had been the one they had directed that statement to? Secondary gains had been brought up in our group sessions several times. Now questions filled my mind. Was that why Dr. Covington asked Scott if he was my knight in shining armor? Had I used my pain as a means of avoiding personal problems? Did I have some suppressed desire to stay in the sick role?

"Did you guys know that you have another new member in your group? She came in this afternoon while you were gone. You'll get a chance to meet her tomorrow. I think you'll be impressed with her. She's elderly, but still very sophisticated looking." Joan was sitting on the edge of Suzy's bed. She had come in to see how our time away from the Clinic was going. "I think she's a little scared right now, but I'm sure the group will make her feel more relaxed once she meets all of you. Now you have a full group; there are five of you."

"What's her name?" Suzy asked, her feet propped up on the bed beside Joan.

"Helen. You're going to have to try to make her feel welcome. She is really scared. Her sister brought her in this afternoon against her wishes." Then she added, "I was very impressed with her manner. She carries herself so straight, stately almost."

"Why is she here?" My voice broke the silence that had fallen over the room, a silence created by Joan's words concerning Helen.

"Some problem with her arm. You'll get a chance to hear all about that in group tomorrow morning. I just wanted you guys to know so you could help her to adjust here, make her feel welcome."

"Well, we'll see," I said as Joan got up and headed toward the door.

"Guess we are filled up now. Oh well. I've been here two weeks tomorrow. Before you know it, I'll be gone. Then what will you do without me?" Suzy jokingly asked.

I did not respond to Suzy's question, and after a brief pause, she quickly said, "I think I'm going to turn in. I had a busy day. See you in the morning."

"Good night."

By now Suzy had managed to join us in sports medicine and physical therapy. Preoccupied by my own problems, I had little time to pay attention to her. She became for me a convenient distraction when I felt like talking. I did feel sorry for her. She was a harmless soul who had lost her way in life. All she needed was love and attention. And after hearing her story in group the other morning, I felt she deserved an uncomplicated life for a while. She had been through a lot with her cancer.

I remained in my chair as the dim night lights in the hall filtered into our room. Time became irrelevant as I sat listening to the distant muffled sounds coming from the nurses' station. My thoughts focused on our newest group member. I could feel myself getting tense because of the way Joan had described her. My old fear of not being good enough surfaced. I somehow felt that I would have to compete with this newest group member and was afraid of being compared with her. Unfounded fear dominated my thoughts as midnight neared.

If I was to feel good about myself, I believed that first everyone else would have to feel positive about me, feel that I was best. I believed Helen would become an obstacle to me as I struggled to maintain the fragment of self-dignity I had left. For the first time in over a week, I wished Scott were there to tell me how much he loved me, how much I meant to him, how important I was.

NOVEMBER 12, MONDAY

As I entered Helen's room on Monday morning, I hoped I would find what Joan had described, and at the same time I hoped I would find someone much more like the rest of us—uncertain, scared, and in need of help. But Joan was right when she had described Helen. She was elegant and stately, but she was also frightened. As I walked into her room I found her sitting on the edge of her bed. She was still in her robe. Her skin was lily white and clear and remarkably smooth for someone of her years. She did have a certain elegance about her, sitting straight, holding her head high, and reflecting wisdom and grace.

Helen did not hear me come into her room, so I tapped on the wall beside her bed to get her attention, saying, "Hello, Helen, my name is Penney. I thought you might like to join the group for breakfast."

With tears quickly forming in her eyes, she replied, "I made a big mistake coming here. I don't belong here. I have too much pain to be put through this program." Helen kept rubbing her right hand, as she spoke. "All I want is another pain pill." She stopped for a moment to look around the room almost as if she were looking for a back door.

Her eyes gazed at the window for an instant. She began to rub harder and harder as her eyes remained fixed on the window in a trancelike state. Helen had begun to change as soon as I had introduced myself. Her body began to tremble and her attention was directed off into space. Her eyes were glassy and hollow as if she had pulled herself into her own private world that only she could reach. Not knowing how to regain her attention and half afraid I would be more destructive than helpful, I turned toward the door saying, "I'll see you later. Sorry I disturbed you," and walked out of the room leaving her to her fantasy world.

"No! I can't go with you! Just leave me alone!" I recognized the voice echoing from the hall; it was David. "Please, just go away . . . just go away."

"Sorry Mrs. Banks, but I'm afraid I'm going to have to ask you to leave. Perhaps you'd like to come into the nurses' lounge with me so we can talk," a nurse requested of an agitated Mrs. Banks.

"Mom, go with her . . . please," I heard David's voice say, his words pleading with his mother.

"All right. I'll leave you alone. You're just an ungrateful little . . ."

The nurse quickly interrupted before she could finish her sentence. "Please, Mrs. Banks, can't we go in here and talk about this?" By this time, they were directly in front of my room. I saw the nurse place her hand on Mrs. Banks's arm and gently direct her toward the nurses' lounge.

Poor David, I thought. He must be feeling total humiliation right now. How could his mother make such a fuss right in the middle of the hall? Why would she do that? Just as I was ready to go to see if there was anything I could do for David, he appeared at my door.

"Can I come in for just a minute?" The look in his eyes was strange. He didn't look like the person I had talked to just a few days before. I was frightened by his appearance.

"What's wrong?" I asked, not really wanting to know.

"I don't want to talk about it right now. I just need to . . . God, I don't know what I need any more." He threw his hands up over his head. "Why can't that woman leave me alone? All she does is nag, nag, nag. I can't seem to make her understand that I am me, not the fantasy that she would like. I am flesh and blood and I have feelings. I have needs, goddamn it!.'' He paused for an instant. He looked directly at me. His eyes seemed to penetrate my flesh. The innocent young boy I had come to know was gone. I thought about the expressions of those portrayed in *Cuckoo's Nest* as his gaze remained fixed on me. ''I'll show that bitch! If I'm not here, what will she do then? She'll have no goddamn son of a bitch to pick on then!''

Without saying another word, David turned and walked out of my room. I felt sorry for him, but at that moment I was happy to see him leave. I promised myself that I would not get involved with any of the other patients on the ward. It was too difficult dealing with my own problems. I did not need anyone else to worry about at this point. But I was afraid for David.

NOVEMBER 13, TUESDAY

Dr. Gabis was generally an understanding person, but occasionally he made it difficult for me to relate to him, probably because I was always aware that behind the friendly compassion I had come to depend on was a professional interest. His white pants and shirt and lab coat always reinforced his medical position. But I was feeling down that morning and hoped that he could spark my determination to continue. David's behavior the night before still haunted my thoughts, even though I had tried to forget. I needed something to get my mind off 7-B.

My hopes for any kind of emotional relief from 7-B quickly vanished as Dr. Gabis began, ''Have you read the book on anger yet?''

''Yes.'' I replied.

''Well?'' His firm jaw protruded as he patiently sat awaiting my response. ''What did you think of it? Could you relate to anything that the book said?''

The entire subject of anger was one I did not really understand. It was only the discussion of the connection between physical pain and anger that had impelled me to read the book. But now it was all lost. I couldn't remember the slightest detail. I felt only emptiness and confusion. "I . . . I . . . guess it was . . . well, I really can't remember too much about it," I said haltingly. I was unable to met his eyes.

"Don't you ever get angry? Don't you ever get so upset, so hurt, so totally frustrated that it becomes impossible to maintain control?"

"I guess so . . . I don't know."

What do you want from me? Should I carry on like David's mother did, or Mrs. Gentry? Should I act crazy and out of control? What do you want from me?

Dr. Gabis sat across from me, his eyes fixed on me, as if he were trying to see right through me. He had the patience of a saint and was willing to allow long periods of silence to fall between us. And often it was the torment of silence that contributed to my saying things I would not otherwise have said.

"All I know about anger is that it hurts. It hurts me and everyone around me." Old hurts came rushing back at me. My mind replayed the all-too-familiar scene of how it had been for me to live in fear of anger, always having to be so cautious about what I said around my parents. Sometimes it would take very little to generate an argument in my parents' home. My role as a child thus became that of "the pleaser." I would do whatever I could to ensure that the needs of others were tended to. I reasoned that if they were comfortable and pleased with a given situation, it was less likely that there would be anger. I guess you can say I walked on egg shells much of my life. I had forgotten about the good times we had had as a family.

"Nothing can be accomplished by anger. Only dogs get mad." The phrase slipped out unintentionally as I turned my head away from Dr. Gabis, afraid to look directly at him.

"Do you honestly think you can remain in the role of peacemaker for the rest of your life? Don't you think that eventually you're going to lose control? People have emotions!" Dr. Gabis exclaimed as he scratched his head.

"I have to try to maintain control. You can't go around spouting off to everyone. People don't like that. No one likes angry people, no one. We have to stay in control. Too many times I felt as if I were the one responsible for the arguments at home. That's why I have to try to please people." The silence once again fell over the room. My mind began racing, thinking of times I had lost my temper, reacted in a negative way, and been properly chastised for it. My tension built as each second passed and the silence remained unbroken.

"No one is going to punish you if you get angry here," Dr. Gabis reassured me with a welcomed interruption. "If you allow negative feelings to build inside of you—and they do build up—eventually your body will have to deal with them, and it might not be in a manner you would choose. Can you understand what I am trying to tell you?"

"Yeah." I understood all too well. My pain had come because I did not get angry, my pain is my anger coming out, and I did it to myself. This is all my fault.

"It might be possible that what you experienced as a child might have confused you. You saw others get angry, and you reacted to them. But when you became angry, you were not allowed to express your anger outwardly. In a way you were living a double standard; anger is okay for your family to express, but not you. I want you to do something for me. One way we have of getting people to at least allow anger to surface in them is to physically express anger. What I want you to do is go over and sit down on your bed. Get in a comfortable position, placing your pillow in front of you."

I did as he asked without question, trusting him to have some very intelligent idea behind his request.

"Now, think back on a situation that really made you angry, one that was so upsetting that it was all but impossible for you to control your anger." Propping his head on his hand, he waited while I sat twenty feet away from him, thinking, thinking, but nothing came to mind. Much in the same way Dr. Covington had tried to get me to verbally express angry feelings at his command, so Dr. Gabis was asking me to do the same thing, to pretend. "You have a clear thought in your mind?"

"No. I just can't pretend to be angry. I can't tell myself, get angry and automatically feel that way. I'm not like that. I'm not!" Frustration was in my every word.

."Yes, you can." He raised his head, looking directly at me, his eyes now unfriendly, impatient, his brow wrinkled, as he demanded in a stern voice, "I want you to hit that pillow. Come down on it with all your might. Pound it!"

"No!"

"Yes! Now!"

"I will feel like a fool. It wouldn't prove anything. I can't do it! I won't!"

"I am not going to leave here until you do! How can you sit there and tell me how you are going to feel before you even attempt it. Don't second-guess yourself. Now!" he insisted with fire in his eyes, his mouth tight, bearing down on his teeth as the muscles in his jaw tightened. "Now!"

BAM! My arms hit the pillow with a loud, crushing blow. My arms ached with pain as they hit the pillow. I raised my eyes, and without words, looked at him; his face was now relaxed, his expression satisfied. I returned the glance. My expression saying, Are you happy now? Will you leave me alone now!

"There. That wasn't so difficult was it?"

"Will you leave now, please?" My voice was low, hollow, as the humiliation grew inside of me. He had forced me to do something I did not want to do. He had controlled me, which made me mad, damn mad.

"Think about what I said. I don't think any less of you for doing that. You have to begin to lose some of that control you try so hard to maintain. Can't you see what it is doing to you? You are like anybody else, and you are allowed to feel like anyone else. Just think about what I said." And he was gone.

But I was not yet done! Not by a long shot! I was furious! As soon as I heard the door close I got the helpless, lifeless pillow and began to beat the stuffing out of it. The more I thought about what he had done to me, the harder I pounded. Each blow brought out more anger. I threw my arms over my head, stopped for a second, but Dr. Gabis's words echoed in my mind. I came down again with a crushing blow. With each exasperated swing, pulsating pain rippled up and down my arms, but it did not deter me from savagely attacking the pillow.

The room filled with the echo of the impact of my fist on the pillow, thump . . . thump . . . thump . . . Each blow grew louder and was more satisfying than the one before. My mind was now focused on nothing but pure and simple anger. As the anger built inside of me, the pounding was not enough to satisfy my need for release and to defy my own rules.

Without thinking, I picked up the pillow and threw it at the closed door. There was no reason, no logic behind my actions. The limp pillow flew, tumbling end over end toward the door, hit it with all the force I could put behind it, and slid to the floor. No longer did I feel a need to explain my actions, even to myself. In spite of my pain, all I felt was a sense of satisfaction, as if that pillow represented a lifetime of hurt and sadness. Throwing the pillow seemed to be a way to destroy and rid myself of all my hurt, resentment, and yes, even anger.

Not until the door of my room opened and a deep, husky voice asked, "Is everything all right in here?" did I regain any awareness of my surroundings.

Humiliation and shame quickly consumed me. My face reddened as I replied apologetically, "Yeah. Everything is all right."

Alone and ashamed, I sat on my bed with my legs pulled tightly against my body and my arms wrapped around my legs.

In spite of the pain, I felt somehow relieved. I had allowed myself for the first time on 7-B to express negative feelings. It just happened, uncontrolled, instinctively, without fore-thought. What might happen as a result of my actions! The stillness of my room was comforting as the relief of letting go spread throughout my body. I remained still and quiet, think-ing of how often I must have wanted or needed to do that, but instead denied myself the pleasure.

NOVEMBER 14, WEDNESDAY

On my initial visit, Dr. Covington had mentioned the possibility of trying pain therapy on me. I had been that route before. I had had those awful injections in my neck every week for a month. They went deep into the muscles, leaving me with a soreness that persisted long after. Moreover, the injec-tions kept me in the role of a patient, a helpless role that, in the past two weeks, I had begun to outgrow.

Pain therapy was on my mind the first week at the Clinic. Then, I was anxious to get it in order to relieve some of my pain. I was willing to put up with the muscle soreness because the overall effect would decrease the pain enough for me to get through those first few days of trying to adjust to my new surroundings.

By the end of the second week, I was no longer willing to go through the motions of complete submission as a pa-tient. I wanted no part of doctors asking questions I had no answers for, no part of being poked and probed from head to toe. I wanted—for the first time in a very long time—to be a person, free from doctors, needles, and all that goes with being a patient. I didn't want to regress. As confused as I was and as much pain as I had, I wanted to continue forward.

The biggest question in my mind was, why were they now sending me down there in the first place? Why would they put me through such risky procedure if I were not worse off than they were telling me? My fear of a continuing deteriora-

tion seemed to be confirmed by their decision to treat me with
the pain-killing drugs. That fear is what made me agree to
another attempt at pain therapy.

On the way down to pain therapy my thoughts were
distracted for a moment. The orderly who was accompanying
me was one of the two who had searched my personal effects
the day I was admitted. He was large and loomed over the
hospital gurney I was lying on. Suddenly, the house phone
in the elevator rang, the noise vibrating in the tiny space. He
picked up the phone, his face taking on a strange look as the
person on the other end began to speak.

"I'm afraid you have the wrong phone. This here is one
in an elevator in the Cleveland Clinic." For a moment he was
silent as he listened again. "No ma'am, this ain't Detroit!
You got the wrong number and this ain't even a phone you
can call on 'less you're in the Clinic. Your line sure did get
messed up, lady." Another silent moment. "Lady, I ain't kidding you . . . I got to get out of this elevator. Good-bye!"
He hung up the phone, and with a grin on his face, he looked at me and shook his head as we headed out of the elevator.

I lay on the gurney outside an old room of the Main Clinic
building. I shivered, wearing only a hospital gown, one thin
bed sheet covering me. A steady stream of people passed by.
Each one turned to look as though I were on exhibit. To them,
I was just a distraction to break the monotony of walking down
the dreary, poorly lit hallway. Time crept slowly by. I remained
flat on my back, helpless, scared, and uncertain. I was a patient waiting for a procedure I did not even believe in.

"Are you familiar with the TENS unit? I'm afraid that's
all we'll be able to offer you because your pain seems to be
so widespread." The doctor spoke in a deep, growling voice.
"There's no way I would subject you to the number of nerve
blocks it would take to get positive results. I'll have the nurse
come in and tell you how it will work and show you how to
care for it." Before I had a chance to respond, he was gone.

I knew from past experience what a TENS unit was. They put small electrical leads onto your back, over specific nerves, depending on where the pain is. Small electrical impulses sent from the control (about the size of a pack of cigarettes) through the wires to the leads plastered to the skin short-circuit the nerves carrying the message of pain to the brain, thereby jamming the signal.

The nurse came in and explained the unit to me as she placed the leads on my back and neck. I felt defeated. Suddenly, I came to a decision: I would not give this unit a chance to work. I would never again allow myself to be so helpless and dependent on doctors and nurses-I would take control of my own well-being by putting in more effort. That morning I finally realized how unhappy I was being a patient. For the first time since my arrival I made a *total* commitment to myself to at least try. All I knew was that I did not want to be a patient any longer!

NOVEMBER 15, THURSDAY

As I scanned the room I saw the same people I had been living with, eating with, and sleeping with for what seemed a lifetime. I saw nothing but blank expressions. The eyes seemed unable to focus on anything other than the floor or the window. Dr. Covington's eyes slowly examined each of us as he waited patiently for one of us to say something, anything.

"You know, unless you people put out some effort to help yourselves and begin to share some of your feelings with me and the other group members, none of you are going to achieve a damn thing." Dr. Covington was no longer willing to accept the total lack of participation. His voice filled with irritation as he continued. "I know for a fact that at least one of you has something very important to talk about and you are unwilling to do so. If you people want to play games, you'd better go somewhere else to do it! I have got more important things to do than sit here and let you waste my time!''

His little speech failed to generate any response. The group remained unresponsive and still. As each second ticked away, the level of tension built, but the silence continued. No one was willing to commit their feelings simply for the sake of releasing the rest of us from the quiet tomb. Time seemed to stand still. There were no words, only occasional glances cast back and forth across the room. Dr. Covington was visibly impatient, and he began tapping his fingertips on the arm of his chair. His eyes moved slowly around the room, examining our faces. But we were locked into a chilling silence.

Suddenly, without hesitating, Dr. Covington stood up and walked out of the room, turning around only slightly to remark, ''Well, I sure hope tomorrow is going to be better than today. Unless each one of you gives this program your all, it could be a very long, hard road for each of us, including me. I'll see you turkeys tomorrow.''

''Suzy, want to step outside? I want to talk with Penney—alone!'' Dr. Covington demanded as he entered our room late that morning.

Suzy left and he turned to me saying, ''What is this crap I hear about your getting up in the middle of the night and yelling?''

''What?''

''You heard me! What is this crap I heard about your getting up in the middle of the night and yelling?'' His expression was solemn, his eyes remained fixed on me. His words rang in my head. He did not move a muscle as he sat there glaring at me. ''Well!''

In a matter of five seconds, hundreds of thoughts flashed through my head. I became confused, doubtful, and scared to death. My voice trembled as I said, ''I swear to God, I don't know what you are talking about!'' His expression was unchanged, his eyes still fixed on me as I continued, my heart racing, ''I didn't! Why are you doing this to me?''

"It's all right here in black and white. Read it for yourself."
He held my chart up in the air as his evidence. "It's all right
here in the nurses' notes. They reported you doing it twice."

Son of a bitch! Why are you doing this to me?

"I'll read it to you." He pulled the chart back down on
his lap as he began to read, "Time: 2:05 A.M. Was lying on
her stomach, pounding her pillow, yelling, 'I hate him, I hate
him!' "

"I can't believe that! My God!" My heart was pounding
rapidly, moisture was forming above my upper lip as my mind
searched frantically for the slightest recollection of the event.
"Why, why would I do something like that?"

"I'm not sure. Perhaps you are so afraid of showing anger
that the only way you can deal with it is by letting it out unconsciously, in the form of a dream. You seem to have a very
distorted view of anger that you refuse to let go of. Don't you
realize that anger is just an emotion? Just like any other emotion you might feel." His voice was calmer now, the tone I
was more used to hearing, but I remained on the edge of my
seat. Soon Dr. Covington's expression became more relaxed
and reassuring as he said, "You know that unless you begin
to recognize your anger and realize that, in fact, you do have
angry feelings, you are headed for big trouble. Anger is not
always bad. Anger is a healthy emotion, as long as it is expressed appropriately. Not expressing it often causes anger to
build up inside of you until you explode, just like what happened to you. You just chose to do it unconsciously. Next time
you might direct it at someone who doesn't deserve it, or you
might continue to turn it in on yourself. You cannot control
your emotions all of the time. You are trying to do that, and
you are finally losing. You have to realize that what you feel
is a part of you.

I was still trying to absorb what he had said. "I still don't
believe I did that. I would have remembered it if I had. I would
have remembered!"

"Well, you did it and you do remember. You are just choosing not to remember."

Without warning he changed the subject, denying me an opportunity to defend myself or understand what was happening. "Why didn't you want to go with Scott this weekend?" he asked nonchalantly.

"Who said I didn't want to go with Scott this weekend?" A feeling of panic overwhelmed me as I spoke. My head began to swim. My head actually began to feel heavy.

He ignored my question, saying, "Go sit on your bed," as if commanding a dog to sit up and bark.

"I can't do it. I can't!" I recalled the same words Dr. Gabis had spoken the other day.

"Do what I said! You want me to help you don't you?" His voice sounded harsh.

"Yes, but."

His eyes followed me as I slowly approached the bed. "Now sit down and put your pillow in front of you. Go on."

"I've already done this. I felt like a complete fool doing it before. This is crazy!" I could sense the level of anxiety building in me. I didn't want to do it, but I was too afraid not to.

"If you can't act crazy here, then where can you? You have nothing to lose. What can we do to you if you act crazy, lock you up?

Perhaps put me in restraints. I'm already locked up.

"This just might help you remember."

As I placed the pillow in front of me, he said, "No, do it like you did it last night. Roll over on your stomach."

"Please!" The mattress beneath me groaned as my body settled down on the bed, my neck unyielding as I tried to turn my head toward him.

"Okay, now hit the pillow with all your might and say, 'I hate him, I hate him,' " he commanded, as if giving directions to an actor.

Once again, it was fear of further humiliation and verbal abuse that forced me to do as directed. My arm broke the invisible screen of air, bouncing off the pillow, as I repeated, "I hate him."

Sitting up quickly so as not to give him an opportunity to ask for another take, and feeling embarrassed, and resentful, I said, "I still don't remember anything."

"You will."

"But what about Scott? Who told you that!" I pleaded, still bothered by his earlier remark. I felt as if my feelings of uncertainty about my love for Scott were visible.

"It doesn't matter," he said as he shrugged his shoulders, his palms up. He walked toward the bed where I was sitting and patted me on the head gently as if that would make all he had just dumped on me go away. It was a reassuring pat to a little lost puppy. "Well, I have to go to a meeting. I'm late already. I'll talk with you later."

Panic consumed me! I cried out, "You can't leave me here like this!"

"You'll be okay. I'll see you tomorrow." And he was gone.

My God, I'm afraid I've finally lost my mind.

Dr. Covington's words echoed in my mind as I sat on my bed. I tried to separate the talking in my sleep and my unwillingness to go with Scott. I needed answers and reassurance —I needed to hear Scott's caring voice. With every ounce of strength I had, I made my way down what seemed an endless corridor. I had to hear from Scott that I had never before done such a ghastly thing. I wanted to hear Scott's voice saying— "Don't worry. You're as sane as the rest of us. I've never known you to talk in your sleep. It's just a tactic he's using."— But just as my fingers reached up to the numbered buttons on the phone, my mind went blank. I forgot the number that I had wanted to call. Nothing! I could not remember his office number. The same number that I had been calling for years had simply disappeared from my head. I felt plagued by uncertainties. Was I losing my mind? Was that what they wanted me to do? Was that how relinquishing control was going to affect me? I had to find out if I had screamed in the middle of the night.

The receiver shook as I replaced it in its cradle. Standing in the hall, I felt as if the entire world had just let me down. I thought of Suzy. She might know if what Dr. Covington said was true. I rushed into the lounge, almost running into one of the psych patients standing at the doorway. There Suzy sat, quietly watching television. "Suzy." I motioned her aside. "Let's go to our room. I have to talk to you."

She looked up from the magazine in her hands and said, "Certainly."

Back in our room, I closed the door. I walked over to the chair, picking up the pillow on my bed as I passed. I pulled the pillow close to my chest as I sat down, hugging it tightly. "Suzy, I have to ask you something." A sense of urgency filled my voice. "Dr. Covington told me . . ." Her expression did not change as I quickly replayed what he had said about the previous night. "Well, do you remember me doing anything like that? Tell me you don't, tell me he made it all up, please." My knuckles were white as I tightly grasped the pillow.

Calmly, with no evidence of emotion in her voice, she said, "Well now, just wait a minute. Come to think of it, you were talking in your sleep last night. Yeah, I do remember you doing that. I thought you knew what the hell you were doin', so no sense in me buttin' in."

"My God. Why didn't you tell me! *Why!*" I stared at her, not fully trusting her.

"Wasn't my place. Like I said, I thought you knew what you were doing. That was your business." She returned my glare.

I knew what anger was at that moment. I was furious with Suzy for not telling me. I was mad as hell at Dr. Covington for leaving me. I could feel my soul being drawn deep into my body. Any sense of sanity had vanished. I needed answers to questions. I needed for someone to help me, to make all this go away. I need Scott to save me from this maddening place.

Scott's reassurance over the phone that night did nothing to ease my mind. I expected him to come and take me home. I thought he would be upset, possibly believing that they were trying to push me over the edge. I had hoped to find an ally in him, but instead I found a deaf ear. Even Deb's words of encouragement when she came to see me at her usual time did nothing to erase the images of my uncontrollable emotions. I decided that I would have to remain in control at all cost now, even if it meant not sleeping. I put all my energy into staying awake. I was terrified that I would repeat my actions if sleep took over my mind.

In the middle of all that had taken place that day, I was confronted with my first biofeedback session. Needless to say it was a total waste of time. My thoughts were all focused on staying in control, remaining aware of every moment and not allowing something as relaxing as biofeedback to take over my mind. Total control was the key and I struggled to maintain it. I refused the sleeping pills that had been ordered for me because I was afraid that they might alter my "normal" behavior.

My troubles seemed to be snowballing—my pounding the pillow, my dream of killing, my anger toward my parents, and my screams in the night, all seemed overwhelming. Sleep was out of the question. I was determined to stay awake.

I could almost see myself as a mouse placed in a maze, 7-B being the maze. With each turn I made, I slowly and painfully found myself in another dead end. No matter which way I turned, there was no way out. I was trapped helplessly inside my mazelike confines with virtually no way of escaping. I seemed to be retracing the same steps over and over, exhausting myself and becoming more frustrated in the end.

As the night wore on, I was unable to fight off the urge to sleep. My mind refused to play the waiting game. In blank moments, dreams quickly dashed across my mind, my own voice screaming loudly in my head to end the struggle. My body ached with pain. I battled the fatigue that was slowly overcoming me. Finally, I gave in to sleep. Without thought, without control, my entire being yielded to unintentional slumber.

NOVEMBER 16, FRIDAY

As the morning light broke through the hazy window, Stella, in her usual manner exclaimed, "Penney, time to get rolling." Hearing her words, my thoughts went immediately to the possibility that the previous night I had given a repeat performance.

"Stella . . . Stella." My voice still groggy as I asked, "Did I . . . was there any . . . report on me last night?" I hoped that she would tell me it had all been a big joke to begin with.

"No. Everything was quiet. You'd better get going if you want breakfast. I'm a little late waking you guys up. Get moving!"

"Well, it looks like Dr. Covington won't be in group this morning," Stella said, walking into the room. "Guess you guys are stuck with me today," she said jokingly, as she sat down by the window. In the sunlight, her brown hair was highlighted with red strands.

He can't make it! What the hell am I supposed to do? He can't make it! Why is he doing this to me? I need him—and he is not here!

A sudden need to scream at all these people surfaced in me. They were meaningless, insignificant people who would not be able to give me the reassurance I had been counting on from Dr. Covington. Unwilling to share my experience with the group, I sat by myself in the corner closest to the door as Carol began the group with an account of her frustrations with her youngest daughter.

"She has always accused me of being responsible for her dad's dying. Can you imagine how terrible that makes me feel! She was only five when he died; she could not possibly have remembered anything about him." Carol's voice reflected the hurt she had had to deal with for the past several years. Her tone was sincere and much softer as she continued. "I have tried to be a good mother. It's not easy being a mother and father both. I just don't know what to do anymore!"

"What made you think of this now, Carol?" Stella asked.

"She called me last night. Seems there is some sort of big dance at school and she wanted a new dress." She paused for a moment, deep in thought. "I would love to get her a new dress. But I just can't see how I can afford it right now. Christmas is coming up and all." That kind of honesty was rare in Carol. Normally she was eager to let us know that she was well off and had no money problem. For Carol to openly admit in group that she did in fact have "normal" problems somehow made me feel closer to her. It was easier for me to relate to someone who had the same human characteristics, the same fears, the same problems as the rest of us.

Reassurance from each of us seemed to ease Carol's mind a little. It was her openness in group that morning that made me believe that sharing my problem with them would somehow give me the same positive reinforcement and peace of mind that Carol had received. With hesitation in my every word, and the unrealistic hope in my mind that they could miraculously make me forget it ever happened, I told them exactly what had happened.

No one really had anything to say about what I had just shared with them. Even Stella suggested that we wait for Dr. Covington to discuss this issue. I felt abandoned by everyone in group that morning, and still very confused and frightened.

Who was it I was supposed to hate? My mind searched for an easy answer. There was none. First I focused on Scott. He had been my first and only love. I knew the night he walked up to me at the student union where he was attending college to ask me for a dance that he would be the one I would marry.

For the most part, I had a basic fear of the opposite sex, going back to eighth grade. I was a Rainbow girl, an organization for girls from twelve to eighteen. Quite often they sponsored dances. Because the organization was made up completely of girls, they had to do the asking. If I was to attend this dance, I would have to ask a boy. My older sister who had been going steady with the same boy for over a year, planned to attend the formal dance.

And, because it was a formal dance, I would be able to go shopping for a wonderful gown, just like Cinderella going to the ball. I had so many exciting thoughts about the dance, I could hardly stand it. It never entered my mind that I would not be able to find a willing partner. I was under the belief that when one's time was right, one automatically got a boyfriend; that it was predetermined if you will.

I was far too shy to come right out and ask a boy face to face. I took the easy way out and wrote a note to the boy who sat in front of me in homeroom. I had explained what kind of dance it was and that I would even furnish the ticket. I sat in homeroom that morning anticipating a positive reaction and dreaming about how wonderful it would be.

When the bell rang to begin our school day, the boy in front of me turned around and handed me a note. I assumed he too was shy and was accepting in the same way he had been invited. In big bold letters written over my words was the word *NO!* I stood there in disbelief. I had not expected that. But being a determined and assuming he probably had other plans, I decided to try someone else.

By the end of that school day I had tried to invite ten different boys, and ten times I got the same NO. It was the last one, however, that I will never forget.

I was coming around the corner from homeroom, where we had checked in at the end of the day for school announcements, and saw a group of boys about twenty feet in front of me. I stopped, afraid to go past them. After all they had all turned me down. I would wait until they were gone.

"She asked you too! God! She is as ugly as a horse's ass!" I heard those words echo down the hall as I stood there. At that moment, I wished I were dead. The entire situation was far too painful to deal with—but I was trapped, for now.

"She asked every boy in this school I think. No one would ever take her out. And she didn't even have the nerve to ask me to my face." A giggle came toward me. Then I could have told her no to her ugly face.

Another boy spoke up. "Hey, Nickel, I mean Penney." The laughs continued for what seemed hours, but was actually only a few seconds. My body was frozen: I could not make myself move. All I could hear were the taunts of those boys—all of them laughing at *me*. I was a real loser. I was ugly. Each boy confirmed that.

Because of that incident, I never again tried to gain the attention of a boy. The hurt I felt swelled until it all but controlled my interaction with boys. I had trouble even making eye contact with a male classmate if I was unlucky enough to be paired up with him on a project. I was terrified of another such ugly reaction, a reaction I knew I could not handle.

I should have been able to talk this over with my mother. I should have been able to return home that day and tell my mother how much I had been hurt. But she was at work—she was always at work. By the time she got home I had buried my feelings, my hurts, my shattered dreams deep inside of me. I never told my mother why I suddenly chose not to go to the dance.

Some years later, I found myself at a dance, one I did not have to be escorted to. And here, in front of me, was a tall, blond, blue-eyed male who actually wanted to dance with me. He spoke softly as he reached out to take my hand. I felt enchanted. As he held me in his arms, leading me across the floor, I felt like the ugly duckling who had just turned into the beautiful swan.

Scott was also drawn to me. I did not understand why, but I would not risk loosing him by trying to find out. I was willing to let him love me as we grew increasingly close over the next few months. There was never an instant that I did not feel completely, head-over-heels in love with him. So how could it be him I hated?

My dad was another story. As I sat and thought about him, I could really not remember much. We had had a distant relationship. He was out of town most of the time, only spending weekends at home. It was difficult for me to get close to him. I was afraid of him. He was one person I know who had no trouble expressing his anger. Far too many times I saw what anger could do. It was ugly, controlling, frightening, and should be avoided at all cost. And every time my mother would say, "You are just like your father," I knew she was telling me, if you continue to be nasty, you will turn out just like him—mean!"

But, he never really did anything to me. He yelled at me, but I felt I deserved it for not anticipating his needs or that of my mother. My mind came up blank. I could see no good reason to truly hate him or Scott. And I would not allow myself to even think of Scotty, my precious little boy.

So the easiest person for me to accept hate for at that point was my father. He was the most removed from my everyday life. I would not have to look him in the eye while on 7-B. If it had to be anyone, I could, for now, accept it being my father. I felt as if the entire world was coming down around me as I dismissed my train of thought.

"I hear you've had a few rough days," Dr. Gabis said as he entered my room. "Want to talk about it?"

"How? How do I talk about something that I don't even remember doing?"

Dr. Gabis sat quietly for a moment, his soft, brown eyes meeting mine. He looked concerned as he said, "Why don't you tell me how you feel about it."

"Afraid!"

"Afraid of what?"

"I'm afraid I'm losing my mind."

The corners of his mouth turned up, a warm smile on his face as he replied, "You are not going crazy. That much I can assure you. You are just having difficulty recognizing what you feel and understanding strange thoughts you've kept to yourself for so long. Why don't you tell me who *you* think you were referring to, who you hate."

At first I looked at him with a shocked expression, uncomfortable that he thought I hated anyone. Then I said, "Well, I'm certain that it's not Scotty, my son, or Scott that I hate. I'm afraid it's my father." Stopping momentarily, hoping Dr. Gabis's expression had not changed, I continued. "He is the one I was so afraid of as a kid. Both my parents controlled my actions. I allowed them to. They both instilled values in me that I believed to be above question. It was their continual remarks, little things they say, that shaped me as a child and that make me so controlled."

"Like what? What are some of the things they told you?"

"God, that's hard to say." Brushing my hair out of my eyes, my fingers running along my scalp, I said, "You know, 'Don't be like that,' 'Children are to be seen and not heard,' 'Only dogs get mad,' 'You're just like your father.' "

"What do you mean, 'Just like your father'?"

"My mother always said he had a terrible temper. If I got mad, she would tell me I was just like him. I didn't want to be like someone I feared because of his anger. No . . . I'm not like him. But she kept telling me I was."

Dr. Gabis cleared his throat as he asked, "You realize you are not like your father, don't you?"

"I don't know. Seems like I'm losing ground. Look what I did the other night." I could feel tears welling up in my eyes. "I am so damned confused! Why . . . Why should I hate them? They'd taken care of me all my life and provided me with all the things I needed. Why would I be so ungrateful? Blood is thicker than water, right?"

"Penney." Dr. Gabis hesitated until I looked at him. "You are just now becoming aware of a lot of emotions you have denied feeling. No one in this world is free of hate. You have to love someone in order to feel enough hurt when they disappoint you to hate them. Sort of a complete circle, love and hate. I think you have a long way to go before you can openly recognize negative emotions. Just allow yourself to feel, without always trying to control those emotions or to analyze them."

"I don't know. I just don't know." I turned away from Dr. Gabis. I felt as if I had betrayed both my parents. "It would kill me to think that some day my children would talk about me in the same way." I fell silent for a moment lost in thought. "I have no right to judge them. I have no right to judge anyone. God, look who ended up in the psych ward. It just has to be *me*. It *has* to be. There is something wrong with me."

I could feel the tears forming in the corners of my eyes, eyes which remained fixed on the floor so that Dr. Gabis would not see that I was about to cry.

"Penney."

"What?"

"Do you really believe all this crap you're telling me?"

"Yes."

"I think that you need to think about what you just said. You need to focus on all the things in your life that you have accomplished. You seem to have a talent for looking at all your bad points. Give yourself a break."

He paused for a moment. Tears were now flowing down my check, but I was unwilling to wipe them away. I did not want him to know that he had made me cry.

"Can't you share with me some of the things you like about yourself? We have all had times in our lives when we are uncertain. And parents never live up to the expectations of their children. I did not totally understand many of my parents' reactions or requests until I was in med school. We do not posses enough experience in life to understand the reasoning behind our parents' judgments. But that does not mean they don't love us, or that we are bad people. Everyone makes mistakes, including parents. You have to be able to let go of your past. You seem to hold on to all the hurts and allow them to consume your mind and your ability to think positively about yourself.''

"I really don't want to talk about this right now," I replied, hoping he would leave me alone until I could regain control of myself. He did.

As Dr. Gabis left my room, an emptiness took over me. Guilt haunted me the remainder of the day.

Not you! I am not in the mood for you now. Go away.

Once again David stood at my door. Suzy was back in the lounge watching television. I was alone in my room and happy to be alone.

"What's up?" I asked David as he approached me. "Is there something wrong? I had hoped he would say 'no' and leave."

"Nothing much; just wanted to see how you were doing." I could smell the scent of something sweet as he sat in the chair beside me. There was a moment of silence before he said, "Did you hear about Pete and Linda? Do you know who they are?"

"I'm not sure. Isn't she the one with the long brown hair?"

"Yeah, that's her. Anyway. I heard that she was foolin' around with Pete. I don't know why she is here. She never really says anything in group. But I do know that she is married. Her husband comes to see her every once in a while. Seems as if she is not real crazy about her husband."

"What do you mean?" I really couldn't have cared less

about what he was telling me, but I did not know how to get rid of him.

"This morning in group the doctor asked her how she felt about Pete. Came right and asked her in front of all of us." David shook his head in disbelief as he continued. "She said that she thought she was in love with him. Not with her husband. I heard some of the other people say they have been sneaking off somewhere in the Clinic and doing things. You know, sex things."

"Well I guess they are old enough to know what they are doing."

"Yeah, but to do it right under everyone's nose! Gosh, that takes some kind of balls! Can't say I would be willing to risk that."

"David?"

"Yeah."

"How are things with you?" I did not want to hear any more about Pete and Linda. Perhaps is was my own insecurities that made me feel uncomfortable with the way the conversation was going. David's immaturity showed in the way he spoke of the two lovers. He reminded me of the way my classmates had joked about my asking them to the dance. 7-B was tough enough without having to cope with rumors.

"Fine," David quickly snapped back at me. He immediately got up and said, "I got to go. I have to do a few things before tomorrow." He walked out the door and suddenly popped his head back in saying, "Thanks for listening to me. It helped." His tone made me think he was really saying good-bye.

I did not find out until two day later that David had left the Clinic. Some of the regular psych patients were allowed the same freedom as the pain patients. David was allowed off the ward whenever he wanted. The story I got from Carol— she somehow knew everything about everyone on the ward— was that on his way to dinner that evening he just walked out. No one has heard from him since. I wondered if he would be able to survive out there by himself. He was so childlike.

I was tense and unsettled. My pain was worse than usual that day. I needed to remember something about my actions. I was building the incident up in my mind so that all my thoughts were focused on trying to remember something that seemed not to exist.

Both my negative feelings and my physical pain increased as the day progressed. By night I was unable to hold my toothbrush. Sharp, shooting pains rippled up my arms and grabbed my shoulders with a savage grip. It took all the effort I could muster to get undressed and crawl into bed. I was so utterly exhausted that I fell asleep within a few seconds of lying down. But before I did, I suddenly understood why I was hurting. As awful as that day was, it was the beginning of an important discovery for me. I began to see the connection between the intensity of my pain and my emotional state.

NOVEMBER 17-18, SATURDAY AND SUNDAY

"No one remembers what happens while they're asleep. I used to talk in my sleep as a kid. It was no big deal," Carol tried to reassure me as group began. "My kids used to talk in their sleep. I never thought anything about it. If I were you, I wouldn't let it bother me."

But you're not me!

"Oh Penney, it was just a little thing. Don't let it get you down," Joyce was quick to reassure me.

"But she does remember, she is just choosing not to." Dr. Covington held fast to his belief that I knew exactly what I was doing in spite of the views of the group.

Throughout most of the weekend, I managed to put the sleeptalking out of my mind. It was still difficult for me to go to sleep at night, however. I lay in bed, in the same place where it had happened, and I couldn't help but think about it then. As difficult as it was, I had to believe that Dr. Covington was right; I did remember, I just chose not to. But during the day I was out of the Clinic and out of the room. I was free, for a while, to forget whatever I wanted to, with no reminders present to trigger such thoughts.

NOVEMBER 19, MONDAY MORNING

"Suzy, want to step out please? We want to talk to Penney alone," Dr. Covington said as he entered our room, Dr. Gabis trailing right behind him.

Oh shit! Now what did I do?

A morbid silence hung over the room while Dr. Covington read my chart. He made a few entries, as he often did. I was afraid to look at either one of them. What had I done this time? And both of them together! Something was terribly wrong!

"We feel that you have come to an impasse in your thinking," Dr. Covington said as he gently guided the metal cover on my chart to its closed position. "We feel that we might have to take a new approach with you. We would like to try something a little different."

"What?" I asked, my hands clenched, knuckles white. God, what were they really after?

"Well, I really believe you're trying to cut through all the confusion you've had recently."

None of which I ever had until I got here.

"What we were thinking of might help us get more information in order to help you."

I tried to get a look at Dr. Gabis, who sat out of my direct vision. Perhaps I could get some indication of what was going on from his expression. Afraid to move a muscle, frozen in my chair, I waited.

"I would like to try to hypnotize you—see if we can't find out what you're having so much trouble with. It's a relatively simple procedure. I don't think we'll have any problems." Dr. Covington spoke matter-of-factly, unaware of the impact his words had on me.

Hypnotize me! My God! No . . . no. Has it come to this?

I opened my mouth to speak, but nothing came out. My body felt weighted, unable to move. My limbs were hot and cold at the same time. I could hardly breathe and my heart raced as I just stared at Dr. Covington, who was now talking with Dr. Gabis. "Yes, it has been done before." Dr. Covington turned back to me.

"There are a few questions I need to ask you." Now taking a clinical tone with me, he said, "Let's see . . . do you often take naps during the day?"

"No."

God, get me out of here! I don't think I can hold on.

"I want you to look straight ahead, eyes open, and see if you can roll your eyes up toward your forehead while your eyes remain open," he said as he demonstrated. His eyes rolled back into their sockets as he was temporarily transformed into an alien being.

I tried, but I just couldn't do it. I was getting rather perturbed at the senseless procedure. I needed facts, reassurance, hope, answers. I asked, "When would you plan on doing this? Can it really help?"

There was no response from either of them. Were they playing some kind of game with me? Had I perhaps lost touch with reality? Was this their way of testing my mental stability? Or was I just becoming so confused it was obvious to them that unless they did something, I would end up lost in my own world, unable to separate reality from fantasy, or love from hate, forever looking for answers that did not exist. My heart continued to race as I conjured up all sorts of "what ifs."

"Do you really think this will help me? What if something
. . . ? or I find out things . . . things I can't . . ."

"Are you going to sit there and intellectualize, try to get
all the answers before the questions have been asked, or are
you going to let us try and help you!" His voice was firm now;
he was irritated with me. "Why do you always have to have
all the answers before you try anything?"

I felt undeserving of his short temper. All I wanted was
to be sure I would be able to handle it, at least get something
out of it, something that would help me, not them. I'm not
sure what it was I really wanted to know, but I was afraid and
felt threatened, and I was reluctant to be so bold as to put
my unconscious thoughts into Dr. Covington's hands. I wasn't
quite that trusting.

"It really doesn't matter; you're not a good candidate."

What the hell does he mean by that?

With no further explanation, he said, "I think I would
rather try Sodium Pentothal on you." Now directing his attention to Dr. Gabis for the first time since he began, he said,
"I think she would do pretty well under Pentothal. Have you
ever seen that?"

"No, but I would like to." For the first time since I entered
7-B, I felt I was once again going to be someone's guinea pig.
The two of them became wrapped up in medical jargon I didn't
understand.

Tell me, not him. I am the one it's going to happen to.

"Well, I think that's the way we'll go on this. How do
you feel about it, Penney?" Finally, he was letting me have
some say in all this.

Both a lack of understanding and pure fear prevented me
from replying right away. Dr. Covington was not willing to
give me much information about the procedure. Why should

I trust him? Why should I allow myself to be put into a situation I might not be able to control? I looked from Dr. Gabis to Dr. Covington. I looked into their eyes, hoping to see something that would reassure me that I could handle it. I turned my eyes to the floor, afraid of any further questions, thinking.

"Well?" Dr. Covington was becoming impatient with me.

I answered haltingly, "I guess . . . if it's the only thing I can do . . . I guess . . . uh . . . I will." Hundreds of questions raced through my mind, but I was apprehensive about asking. I hoped that he would tell me more after I gave the go-ahead.

Without giving me any more details, aside from saying they would let me know when they would do it, they left the room. I had to wonder why the other group members didn't have all this stuff going on with them. Why Me?

NOVEMBER 19, MONDAY EVENING

Finding even a few moments of quiet time on 7-B was difficult. I was hoping that Suzy would visit with Carol and Joyce, which would give me much-needed solitude, time to think about my life. I needed to gain insight into exactly what event in my life was the turning point. Who or what had brought me to my present state? And who had had the most impact on my personality?

Fortunately, Suzy was finally making an attempt to read *The Angry Book*. She sat quietly off by herself in the corner of the room, absorbed in the contents of the book. I sat directly opposite her, on the other side of the wooden table, when I heard loud voices in the hall.

As the voices grew louder, I got up and walked to the doorway to investigate. Near the end of the hall, inside the door, stood three men in business suits, and two men wearing uniforms like those of the guards who stand by the elevators checking passes. I wondered what they were doing up here.

Once they disappeared into the first room on the left, the noise subsided. Suzy came toward the door now, limping because of her sore knee and almost losing her balance as she neared the door. But the commotion had been too loud for her to ignore. As she joined me, we exchanged perplexed looks. Was one of the patients so violent that the nurses needed to call security? Or had someone done themselves in? Anything was possible there.

We must have stood there about ten minutes. Suzy, unsteady on her feet, leaned against the wall for support. Soon the door opened and out walked the five men and Stella. They huddled near the door, talking and gesturing excitedly for a while. I had to satisfy my curiosity. As Stella let the men out of the ward, I walked toward her, motioning for her to come to me.

"What was going on?"

"I really can't tell you. Everything is all right now. Don't worry about it." Stella was not about to give any explanation of what had happened. She turned and left us standing in the dreary hall of 7-B, wondering.

NOVEMBER 20, TUESDAY

Lizzy was our new group member and soon to be Helen's new roommate. Her nasal sound filled the room. "God, you should have seen them run when they found the gun in my purse. You'd have thought they had never seen one before!" Lizzy didn't wait for Stella to come into group before introducing herself. She was anything but shy! Before we knew what hit us, Lizzy was giving us a blow-by-blow description of what had happened the previous night.

"Everything was cool until they decided to check out my purse. Man, when that gun came falling out on the bed— you should have seen old Stella! Her mouth was hanging open, she didn't know what the hell to do. Then all of a sudden she shoots out the door. 'Fore I knew what the hell hit me, all these men come running into my room . . . all talking at once. Jesus! It was funny! Hell, I wouldn't go anywhere without my gun. No way in hell! And this place most of all. But what the hell. It's in the safe downstairs. I'll get it before I leave this joint."

I felt as if I were listening to a new inmate talking. She was hard looking, her tight black jersey accenting her full bosom. She had rings on every finger and more chains than I could count hanging around her neck. Her hair was in tight curls, and she carried a hair pick in her hip pocket. She didn't appear to be more than thirty-five at most, but she wore so much makeup it was hard to tell. Her eyes were ringed by dark blue eye shadow that added to her street look. She was so nonchalant about her gun. No big deal. To look at her you would never know she had any kind of pain problem. Her body was in constant motion, with legs shaking and fingers tapping nonstop on the arm of the chair.

That first morning in group, Lizzy didn't act like the rest of us had: quiet, afraid, timid. She was outspoken. She did not separate the psych ward from the pain unit. She considered herself to be in the loony bin and that was that. Lizzy was one of a kind, different, brash.

I felt intimidated by her, not so much by her mannerisms but because she was so free. She was completely uninhibited in what she said and did. What made her that way? What gave her the confidence to be so open? Lizzy would be someone we would all have to reckon with. She added variety to our rather low-keyed, solemn group. I just couldn't believe what I was seeing and hearing! Lizzy was evidence that our group was a combination of ages, lifestyles, and values.

I was drawn to Lizzy because she was different. I had to get to know her better; she fascinated me. She appeared to be so hard, as though nothing could affect her, as though there was nothing she hadn't tried. At the age of thirty-five she had been married three times, divorced three times, and had a sixteen-year-old and eighteen-year-old daughter. "That," I thought admiringly, "had to take some doing on her part!" She was one of those people I had never understood and had never really accepted. Her way of life was the complete opposite of mine. I needed security and an organized, stable sort of life; Lizzy seemed to thrive on turbulence. Her life was like a tornado with all its parts caught in the whirlwind, while mine was totally predictable. In my struggle with myself, I was open to a new view on life, and Lizzy certainly shed some light on a way of life I had only read about or seen portrayed in the movies. She was the catalyst that our otherwise humdrum group needed.

When our first assertiveness class began, Lizzy tried to show her tough, independent nature. She was not about to accept their ideas about assertion. She didn't have to—she knew how to assert herself. She could take care of herself and make her needs known without the lectures. I had no doubt that she usually got what she wanted.

"The only kind of assertiveness I need is my little old gun. Damn men don't know when to quit! Hell, when I leave a bar at night by myself, all I do is put my hand inside my purse, one finger on the trigger, and waltz on out to my car. Just let someone try and mess with me!" Lizzy had fire in her eyes as she shared her assertiveness trick.

Cheryl, the nurse who led the classes, commented, "Well, Lizzy, that might work for you. But I'm afraid we have to talk about our everyday lives in here. We try to discuss ways to help all of you take some responsibility for your actions."

Lizzy just laughed at that, saying, "I *am* talking about my everyday life!"

"You know, I think Cheryl is right," Carol explained. "We all have to be able to say no to people. I don't have any trouble getting what I want. I took a class at the university in assertiveness, you know. There is a lot to be said for this stuff. I don't let anyone walk all over me!" The personality

Carol had exhibited her first day in group—shy, timid, and afraid—had vanished. If what Carol said was true, then why did people dump on her? She continued in a voice that cut through the air. "You can certainly get your point across without such violence! Saying no is easy if you do it enough. Ask my kids, they'll tell you. No one pulls nothing on me anymore!" Her words lingered long after her voice was still.

NOVEMBER 21, WEDNESDAY

I once again had to face the here and now and become aware of my thoughts and my surroundings. I patiently sat through group and listened to Carol praise herself. She did exaggerate, but she was in fact making progress rapidly and I resented her a little for it. Dr. Covington tried to help Helen get in touch with the feelings of resentment and abandonment her father's death had created. (Helen had told the group just two days earlier about her father, the closeness they shared, and the total devastation she felt when he passed away. She had devoted her life to him, never marrying, just taking care of him until he died before she was ready to accept his death.) I heard Joyce insist the pain in her face was the only problem in her life, even though you could see the emptiness she felt since her children had left home. But I didn't really care. Who were these people anyway? What did I need them for? Why should I care about their feelings? I had my last chance to help myself coming up.

Minutes after group broke up, it was time for the Pentothal. I had by now accepted the idea of the procedure, hoping it might provide me with enough answers to clear up the lingering questions that plagued me continually. I really believed that if I could gain such understanding my pain would disappear.

I lay on my bed as the room filled with six or seven people. Only Dr. Gabis and Dr. Covington were familiar to me.

It was difficult enough knowing both of them would be privy to my innermost thoughts, but why did they have to ask all these others? Or were they just curiosity seekers, anxiously waiting to witness my self-betrayal? Apprehensively, I awaited the state of consciousness the Pentothal would create.

Moments after the last doctor entered the room, now ten in total, Dr. Covington walked toward me. He looked at me compassionately as he touched my arm and said, "We're just going to inject enough of this medicine into your vein so that we can still talk to you. You won't be completely knocked out. You'll do fine. Right, turkey?"

With that I smiled as he tied the tourniquet tightly around my arm and said, "Make a tight fist for me."

I immediately felt a throbbing in my arm and then the needle punctured my skin. I heard Dr. Covington tell me, "Just start talking until you feel sleepy."

"Yesterday." I took a deep breath. "I think it was yesterday that I . . . (My chest was heavy, as if someone had put many blankets on top of me, making it a struggle to breathe, each breath more labored than the one before. My eyes remained closed as if magnets were holding them shut.)

It seemed like only a minute had passed when I heard Dr. Covington's voice. "Penney, I am going to take the needle out."

No . . . no, . . . you didn't give me a chance to say anything . . . no . . .

I was sure that not enough time had passed to allow them to get to the bottom of my mind, my subconscious. I felt cheated. I heard someone in the distance say something, but it didn't register. I went out again.

The remainder of that day was a blank. I lost track of time. Occasionally I woke and glanced at my watch, but I did not really care what was going on. I slept the entire day, not even caring about what had taken place during my Pentothal interview.

It was early evening when I heard Dr. Gabis's voice. As he walked past my bed toward the door, I said in a low, sleepy voice, "Did you find out what you wanted?"

"We didn't get any new information." His voice was distant and filled with disappointment. I shared the feeling.

NOVEMBER 22, THURSDAY

Today was Thanksgiving. A time to give thanks for the many blessings in one's life. A time to remember things that would automatically bring a smile. This day was to serve as a reminder to all how much our forefathers had sacrificed to build this great country of ours.

Give thanks for what?

As I opened my eyes that cold November morning, there was no anticipation in my heart. I had no excitement. I felt lost my final battle, or so I thought. Through my groggy recollection, I could still hear Dr. Gabis say, "No new information." My thoughts held what I believed to be the key to my future. I had been convinced that my emotions played a significant role in my recovery and that all I had to do was call upon them to give me the answers I needed so that I might live, not merely exist as I had been doing for the past six years. The only problem was that those very thoughts that could free me were unreachable. I could not examine them rationally, consciously. Now even my unconscious would not let go of them.

Give thanks for what? Being alive? My good health? My peace of mind? My ability to love others? My intelligence? My children? My husband? Was it for being on 7-B?

"Penney, come on. We don't want to keep Scott waiting," Suzy said as she hobbled into the bathroom. Her clothes hung over her right arm, toothbrush sticking out from beneath the clothes. She was excited. She was looking forward to today. She was joining us at Deb's house for dinner. Sam had returned to Texas the week before leaving her all alone. I asked Deb it was all right for Suzy to join us.

"Yes, I am," I replied as I stared blankly into space, one small insignificant person trying to remember all of my yesterdays.

Suzy paced the floor impatiently waiting for Scott to arrive. I remained silent, sitting in the far corner of our room trying to remember.

Give thanks for what?

Just as I thought, Deb had put a great deal of time and effort into preparing dinner: turkey and all the trimmings. I just picked at what was on my plate. I could not forget the previous day's failure. I felt I had come to the end of the road.

Give thanks for what?

The day became even more difficult for me when Scott told me he had planned a trip for us as soon as I returned home. On his own, without asking me, he had made arrangements for us to go to Aruba. I was angry that he had not asked me, and at that moment I had no desire to go. But I thanked him and said nothing.

Give thanks for what?

NOVEMBER 23, FRIDAY

With most of the staff gone from the unit because of the holiday weekend, it proved to be a rather quiet day. I was happy for that. I needed time to think. It was not until that evening that I was once again challenged.

"Penney," Dr. Gabis said as he walked into our room. "Do you want to wait back in the lounge while I talk with Suzy? When I'm done with her, I want to talk with you."

"Okay," I said and headed back toward the lounge.

I sat by myself waiting for Dr. Gabis. Off in the distance I heard several of the other patients talking about something that had taken place in Iran—Americans had been held hostage for several weeks now. What were they talking about?

A few minutes turned out to be a forty-five-minute wait before Suzy appeared at the door of the lounge and told me Dr. Gabis was waiting to see me. I passed her on my way out the door and she gave me a look of disgust saying, "I'm leaving here next week . . . for sure. Good luck to you."

As I walked into the room, Dr. Gabis pointed to the empty chair and said, "Have a seat. Sorry about it being so late, but I've been filling in for several of the other residents on another floor."

I'm not sure what I expected to happen next. My mind was still trying to reach deep into itself to pull something from the past that might explain everything. I was willing at this point to look at anyone in my life to pin it on. In the time I had been on 7-B, I was beginning to feel that I was the one getting the short end of the stick. Although I repeatedly said it was me who was all messed up, I was, nevertheless, becoming painfully aware that others in my life had contributed to my state of mind.

The Pentothal interview should have brought out the real reason for my inability to feel good about myself. Somewhere back in my past there must have been a very traumatic experience that had changed my personality. What was it?

On occasion my mother and dad would jokingly tell me that if you wanted to know what was going on in the building, you just asked Penney, who knew everyone and everything. We lived in an apartment building until I was in fourth grade. There were always people coming and going; the halls of the building were alive with noise. I assumed everyone in the world lived in large buildings like mine. During that period of my life I was apparently very outgoing, talking with anyone who would stop long enough to listen, whether I knew them or not. People were always coming up to my parents and asking them if they were Penney's parents. But I never could remember being that way. Whenever they spoke of these events, I would get uneasy. It was as if a part of my memory had been erased. What did I say to those strangers? How could I have been so comfortable to approach those people? Why did everyone know me?

As far back as I could remember, I had been uncomfortable around people. I was self-conscious about my size, always a head taller than other kids my age and twenty pounds heavier than I should have been. I was the first kid in first grade to get glasses, which made me stand out even more. So where did this story come from? What had happened to me many years ago to change my personality so? I was counting on the Pentothal to unlock that mystery.

I could not clear my mind of these questions as I waited for Dr. Gabis to speak. Here, at the Clinic, was my opportunity to find out who I really was. It was their responsibility to give me the answers. After all, they were the ones who wanted me to remember, to understand myself. I had only agreed to get rid of my pain, not discover things about myself that had been buried all these years. It was up to them. So I asked, "What are you going to do now?" I thought it a perfectly innocent question. A legitimate question under the circumstances.

"We don't go anywhere." Dr. Gabis's voice was distant and unfeeling. "The ball is in your court. There is absolutely nothing more I can do for you."

What! Noooooooooo!

"What am I supposed to do now?" The sound of my heart beat pounding in my ear. A warm sensation spread throughout my body with every passing second. He had to answer—it was his job to tell me! "You guys can't just let go now. Not now!"

"You have to think for yourself. I can't tell you what to do! If things should not go the way you want them to, you would blame me for your misfortune, for treating you wrong. Just like you've done all your life. Always looking to place blame on others for your own mistakes. It's about time you think for yourself. Start to take responsibility for yourself and your actions." Dr. Gabis seemed like a different person all a the sudden. I would have expected that kind of blunt reaction from Dr. Covington, but not him. "We have done all we can for you. You are going to have to do things for yourself and begin to think for yourself. Stop living like your life is sitting on a pile of egg shells. You have got to put out a lot more than you have been."

You son of a bitch! I am trying!

"Think about what you're going to do now. Stop trying to get all the answers before you define the question. I get the feeling that you're giving up, that you feel you've done all you can. That's not true. There's a great deal left for you to do. We cannot do it. Now it is up to you . . . and I'm not sure you're willing to go the distance. We have done all we can." His voice still firm.

My God . . . he's giving up on me. I think he's getting ready to kick me out!

"You know you have as much opportunity as anyone else to recognize and deal with situations in life. Nothing is so black and white that you don't have the ability to work out a solution for yourself."

I heard Dr. Gabis's words, but my mind heard something entirely different. What I heard was: "We are giving up on you. You are not cooperating, so there is nothing we can do.

You must leave to make room for others, who would be more willing to remember." I was furious! My first instinct was to call Scott. I wanted to get away from the Clinic and the damn people on this unit as quickly as possible.

Get out now. There is nothing else to do. You have failed once again.

I wanted to express my feelings to him—yell at him, hit him, hurt him as he had just hurt me. The room seemed to close in on me as I sat there in silence, feeling very much alone, unwanted, unloved, and a complete failure. I was not strong enough emotionally to confront him. He was the one with my life in his hands at that moment and it would be up to him to reach out to me. I had nothing left to fight with. I felt the air heavy on my chest, making each breath difficult, my body willing to succumb to the struggle, allowing the breath to drain out of me without fighting back, while the pounding in my ear grew louder.

Where did that little girl go? What happened to her? God help me . . . I'm lost.

"Penney? Penney?" I heard a distant voice calling my name, echoing through the emptiness of my mind. "Penney?"

Let me alone. Shut up!

"Penney?" I raised my head slowly in response to his words. "Are you all right? You seemed to be somewhere else. Didn't you hear what I said?"

"What?" The air filled my lungs as I answered.

"I said that Dr. Covington and I have discussed this and we would like to try some new therapy on you next week . . ."

"A what?"

"A new type of therapy that might help you to regain some of your innermost feelings."

"But . . . I thought you said you had done all you could. The Pentothal didn't work." My mind was confused. "What else can . . . I do?" I had almost said you.

"I'll tell you about it on Monday."

I was so upset and angry with him, I didn't know how to react, so I simply said, "Okay." I knew that I was doing exactly what he had just accused me of: denying feelings and unwilling to say what I felt. But the name of the game for me was still peace and acceptance. I stared blankly into space as my mind raced to suppress the past few minutes with Dr. Gabis. I was not aware at the time how good I was at doing that. Within a few seconds I heard Dr. Gabis say, "What are your plans for the rest of the weekend?" as if the previous conversation had not taken place.

Regaining my composure quickly, I explained, "Scott went home to be with the kids. Deb and I have plans to do some Christmas shopping." My voice cracking as I spoke.

"Well, have a good time and I'll see you on Monday. Chin up."

It wasn't until Suzy retired for the night that I had time to think about my conversation with Dr. Gabis. There had been many times while on 7-B that I would have gladly given up, but there was something inside of me that would not let go, a force I could not fight. I recalled part of the conversation with Dr. Gabis. I can't tell you what to do . . ."

Yes, it made sense to me. I was willing to take the lead of others. Why not? I put everyone's opinion above my own. In my mind's eye I saw a little girl, me. She was twelve years old, fat, ugly, and dumb. I could feel the hurt in her heart as she caught a glimpse of herself. What a loser. She had to be wrong. Everyone else was right.

Dr. Gabis hit a nerve that night, probably without even knowing it. When I asked him to tell me what to do, I never really gave it much thought. It was a natural reaction on my part. But his answer really made me think. For the first time, I realized I was asking him to make my decisions for me, much as I had done with my parents. When it didn't work out, I could always blame them. Why didn't I ever see that before? In essence, he was telling me to grow up and take responsibility for my own actions. I wasn't that twelve-year-old girl anymore. I was a woman who had to grow up.

I thought about that off and on all night. How many times had I blamed others because I let them make my mind up for me? How many times had I gone over events in the past, only to blame someone else for a situation not working out? It is hard to see oneself through another's eyes, but that is what happened that night. I saw myself through the eyes of my parents, who tried to help by giving me advice when I asked, then blaming them when things went wrong. So many times I did carry resentment for my parents because my life, my efforts, my plans did not turn out as I had hoped. Did my parents fail me or did I fail them?

Even though I was angry with Dr. Gabis for scaring me by letting me think he was going to release me prematurely, he got me closer to understanding what might have been a factor in developing my attitudes. I never let him know how much I got out of what he said. There was still too much I didn't understand, too much pain, both physical and emotional, to get all excited over a small step.

NOVEMBER 24, SATURDAY

"I'm going home, first of next week. I'll wait for Dr. Covington to get back and then it's out the door for me." Suzy sounded angry. "There is nothing else for me here. Dr. Covington said it would be four weeks, and come Monday it will be four weeks to the day. It's time to go!"

"Did Dr. Gabis say something to you the other night?" I knew she had seemed different after her talk with him, but I had been too busy thinking about myself to really give her much thought. I suddenly felt very afraid for her. How did she know it was time?

After thinking about Suzy that night, I realized that she was not leaving because she had improved but because she was running away from something she did not want to face. Something too painful to face. Even more painful than the pain itself. But she would make the final decision. Just as that unknown force inside of me helped me to continue here, Suzy must have had a force in her that pulled her away from the one place that could help her. I must admit, I was anxious to see how Dr. Covington would react.

I hoped that being away from the Clinic for a while would give me a chance to build up a little emotional strength for the coming week. I wanted not to have to work on my feelings. I just wanted to be me, and I knew Deb would accept that.

We went to a mall about a half hour from the Clinic, but I bought nothing. Unanswered questions kept running through my mind. I just wanted to escape from myself, an empty fantasy. I knew I would have to participate in the hours that filled the weekend. I was glad to have Deb to keep me company; her support did help a little. I tried my best to appear interested, but I mostly waited for Monday, when I would find out what kind of new therapy awaited me.

NOVEMBER 26, MONDAY

"Hell, I ain't gonna get out of here till hell freezes over! No way's Ed gonna let someone as crazy as me go." Lizzy had only been there a week and already she complained that it felt like forever. 7-B was like that. After only two or three days, it felt as if nothing else existed, as if you had always been there. Lizzy had become very comfortable there. She was happy to oblige Dr. Covington by calling him Ed. He told all of us to call him Ed, but it just didn't feel right to me and I could never do it. I don't think I would have been able to see him as my doctor if I had allowed myself such familiarities. Suzy couldn't bring herself to call him Ed either, so she called him Dr. Ed. She tried calling him "Sir," until he told her to stop. Dr. Covington was different, and he managed to make even the worst circumstances easier by his down-to-earth attitude. He wasn't stuffy, and Lizzy took full advantage of it.

When the group formed, Suzy began. "Well, me and Sam decided it is time for me to go home. I am much better now. Before I came here all I did was stay on the couch. I even kept the curtains shut because I didn't want to see the outside. I'm better now. It is time for me to leave." Thus Suzy tried her story out on the group before Dr. Covington got there. It was as if she was trying to first convince us, or maybe even herself. She nodded her head as she said, "It's time. Sam is ready to take me home."

I really didn't care about Suzy leaving as my thoughts went back to the long days before I came to the Clinic. The hours spent alone in my bedroom with nothing to do but watch television. There was more to life. There had to be. Perhaps Suzy had fulfilled most of her life's dreams. Maybe there was nothing left for her to do but spend the remaining years of her life with Sam. She was in her golden years and no longer had to strive to achieve.

I asked myself, Do we grow up, get married, have kids, and then die? Is that what life is all about? No. I was not willing to accept that. There was something out there waiting for me. I had no idea what it was, but there was something, and I was determined to find it. I had been exposed to too much on 7-B. My opinion of others was becoming less critical. I had gotten to know a few of the psych patients, the ones I feared so on admission, and they were just like anyone else. They had feelings, too.

I thought again about David. I was not sure if they ever found him. No one really talked about him anymore. It was as if he had never been there. But he was there and he did matter. I mattered, too. My mind slipped back to my childhood once again as the voices in the room faded away.

The hours I put into studying never seemed to pay off. I would sit for hours trying to remember what I had read but nothing stayed in my mind. I had a low self-esteem as it was, so my poor grades were just another thing to dislike about myself.

I often wondered why my parents never said anything to me about my grades. Did they know something I didn't? Was there something wrong with me? Or didn't they care? Dr. Covington asked me that the day I met him. He said I told him that in what I said. All the other kids in school hated report card day. They knew they would have to answer to their parents. I could not remember ever being afraid to take home my report card, as bad as it was. Didn't they care?

A nice quiet girl. No trouble. Did what she was told. Didn't have to be smart to behave. Nice quiet big girl.

"Hi, turkeys," Dr. Covington said as he walked into the room. His words broke the silent distance I had placed between myself and the group. But I could still feel the pain inside of me: how much I wanted someone to care. Dr. Covington continued. "So, how was your holiday? I'm sure you're all happy to get back to work, right?"

"I had a real nice time, Sir." Suzy didn't realize he was joking. Without hesitation, she began to explain to him why she felt she was ready to go home.

Dr. Covington agreed that Suzy could leave the next day. As I thought, Suzy had made the final decision. She would call Sam that night.

I sat in group that morning looking at each person. One by one, I drew mental pictures of their characters as they had shown themselves so far. Helen was the quietest of us all. Once she got used to being there, she seemed to be trying to live up to Joan's description of her as sophisticated. She was gentle, kind, and easy to like. Helen was someone you would like to have as a friend, provided you didn't expect much. She never presented a threat to a superficial friendship. She always had a kind word for everyone, but after a week in the hospital, she still had not really said much about herself. She had only given a few general details of the way her life once was. She said nothing that would clearly define who she was. She devoted her whole life to her work as a secretary, and taking care of her father. Only once had she mentioned a man in her life, and then it was only in passing. Yet I saw the look on her face as she talked about a love affair of many years ago, the gleam in her eyes as she spoke of him, never mentioning his name. Helen had been in love only once in her life and she still seemed to carry that love for that man.

Joyce was like Helen in many respects; she was quiet for the most part, but unlike Helen, Joyce was enthusiastic about everything and always put out every ounce of energy she had, and then some. In exercise classes she always did a few more stretches for good measure, while the rest of us sat lifeless on the mat, amazed at her energy. Yet Joyce, like Helen, did not share her true feelings with us. She often talked about the demands placed on her as a mother and wife. But when asked if it made her angry, she would say that it was her duty to take care of the house, the kids, and her husband. It was apparent to everyone but Joyce that she was trying to get out from under the demanding routine of home, to devote some time to herself.

Carol was always bringing up her diagnosis, degenerative disc disease. She reminded us every chance she got that she had been told she would never walk again and would remain in a wheelchair the rest of her life. She always followed it with, "I wish they were here now, those damn doctors. They would have let me spend the rest of my life in that damn wheelchair. I have one stop to make when I get home!" She had a right to be angry, but after hearing the story for the tenth time, it began to wear a little thin. Carol, along with Lizzy, dominated much of the group conversation. I was talking more, but I still got a pang of anger every time Carol led the conversation to expound on what a great person she was. She really got under my skin!

Lizzy started off each group with one of her off-color jokes. Sometimes they were downright vulgar. Some I didn't even understand. She kept us intrigued the entire time she was there, if only because she was so different from us. I must admit, in a way I admired her and her sense of freedom to do and say as she pleased. She placed no restrictions on herself. I wished I could be as freed as she.

I was brought back to reality by Dr. Covington's closing statement, the same thing he said at the end of each group. "See you turkeys tomorrow."

The new therapy Dr. Gabis wanted to try was something he called the empty chair. It sounded a little crazy to me and I seriously doubted if I would be successful with it.

"What I want you to do is look at that chair." He pulled the chair out from the desk and sat it in front of me. We were sitting by the window in my room. "Imagine that your mother is sitting in the chair. She is telling you what to think and what to feel. I want you to tell her exactly how you feel about her. Let her know that she is not the one who is controlling you any longer. Get angry at her. Express that anger to her."

I looked at him and realized I would not be able to do it. I could not pretend. I had tried that with Dr. Covington previously without success. Why were they focusing in on my mother? Why was she always the one I had to tell off? My God, she was my mother! I was raised to respect my parents, believe what they said, and never question them. I had adopted their way of thinking. I didn't know where to start. What could I say? How does one go about telling their mother off, real or pretend?

As I looked at the empty chair before me, my mind conjured up an image of my mother, though I don't think it was
the kind of image Dr. Gabis was hoping for. I saw before me
a woman who had worked hard all her life. Her expression
was sad, almost lost, as her big brown eyes looked directly at
me. I could feel her sadness.

"I'll start you off since you seem to be having trouble.
Penney, get that chip off your shoulder. Stop feeling sorry for
yourself and do something. You are just like your father
sometimes when you get this way. The littlest thing gets you
mad and you fly off the handle! You want to be like him?
Then just keep it up!"

I sat there looking at the empty chair. The vision of my
mother quickly faded away as I listened to the words, words
that came at me from a distance. I could not react to Dr.
Gabis's words. "Penney, I mean it. I don't want you to be
like that!" A silence fell over the room. Then Dr. Gabis said,
"If you don't watch out, you're going to end up with nothing.
You have to do what I tell you. You have to feel the way I
tell you to."

"Shut up! Shut up! I am me! I am me!" I looked at the
empty chair and realized that even without my mother sitting there I felt such guilt responding to her that way. But
Dr. Gabis's words had hit struck a chord. I had been told all
my life not to be that way. What, what is "that" way? "I
can't do this. Please . . . I can't. It's not my mother, it's me.
I can't blame anyone else for me being screwed up. It is always
me," I said after a moment of silence.

"Why are you so quick to take responsibility for someone
else? Life is real and so are your feelings. Your feelings don't
have to be controlled. There is no way that you can control
what you feel. Feelings come naturally. They are internal
responses to external situations. There are no wrong feelings,
only inappropriate actions. You have a right to think for
yourself now. You always have. Your mother is not living in
your head. It is about time you get her out of there. You make

the decisions. You set the rules to the game. You determine
your own values. Her being in your head as a part of your subconscious creates a lot of unnecessary guilt in you. Be who you
are. I really believe you are capable of that. You are smart
enough to live your own life." Dr. Gabis spoke sincerely. The
tone of his voice, and the look in his eyes told me that what
he said had great merit.

But I had to be the one to feel that way. I had to be the
one to come to terms with my mother and all the values,
distorted or otherwise, that she had taught me. I had to be
the one to discard the hold she had over me, as both Dr. Gabis
and Dr. Covington had suggested believing that regaining control of my thoughts was a big part of my recovery. Allow feelings to surface without first running everything through my
mind using my mother's values? Could I do that?

NOVEMBER 26, MONDAY EVENING

I had been in the same room for biofeedback training the
day I became so upset about my sleeptalking. That day no
amount of relaxation exercises could have settled me down;
I had rejected the idea of biofeedback before walking into the
room. Part of my rejection was related to a past experience.
About three years before, after a series of nerve blocks had
been only partially successful, the one remaining option was
biofeedback. But no one had explained how it worked and
I was discouraged by the number of years my pain had persisted, seriously doubted that anything could really eliminate
it. My understanding of biofeedback was that I would control
my own pain through learned skills. I thought that if I had
been capable of controlling my body, I certainly would have
been doing so all along.

I remained just as skeptical when considering it for the third
time. Supposedly, this biofeedback training was to help me
relieve tension in my muscles, which was supposed to reduce

my level of pain. So there I was again, sitting in the small room, surrounded by strange devices that looked like stereo equipment. I was sitting in a massive chair, contoured to the shape of my body. Al, the biofeedback therapist for the pain group, was by far the softest-speaking man I had ever encountered. His gentle voice was somehow mesmerizing.

But before he could lead me through an exercise, I had to be hooked up to the equipment. A device was attached to my second and fourth finger to enable him to keep a running record of my skin temperature. More wires with small round electrodes were placed on my forehead to record the tension in my muscles. It all seemed rather strange. I couldn't see how being attached to this ridiculous machine would help me understand myself or diminish my pain. Once I was wired up, Al dimmed the lights even further and gave me a minute to sit quietly and try to relax. Under the circumstances that was rather difficult.

"This is a program for deep relaxation, to help you experience a growing sense of peace in both your mind and body that will refresh you. The instructions I am going to give you are easy, so you should have no trouble following them. Simply listen to my voice and allow your mind and body to respond naturally, without any effort . . . You can use my words as a guide for your feelings and sensations . . . Usually it is important to be in a comfortable position . . . When you practice at home, wear loose clothing and allow yourself to be as completely supported as possible by the chair."

I began thinking about how the chair felt under me.

"Just begin to feel your arms, legs, and shoulders relaxing. Just feel them loosen and relax. Now open your mouth for a moment and move your lower jaw from side to side very slowly and very gently. Now close your mouth slowly, keeping your jaw slightly apart."

That was the first time I had ever been aware of the amount of tension in my face when I held my teeth clenched. I could feel the difference by allowing my jaw to remain slightly apart.

"With your shoulders loose and relaxed, turn your head from side to side, letting the muscles of your shoulders and the back of your neck relax, very slowly and very evenly in a smooth fluid motion. . . . Now facing forward, sense relaxation in your face . . . your loose jaw . . . your neck and shoulders. . . . With your lips closed, feel your jaw hang loose. . . . Let it drop naturally. . . . Feel the tension flowing from your upper body. . . . Take a deep breath. . . . Feel your lungs filling with air. . . . Hold it a moment. . . . Now, let the air flow naturally from your lungs so that your chest feels loose and relaxed. . . . As you exhale, let your shoulders and upper arms follow as well. . . . Once again, take a deep breath, deeper then before. . . . Hold it a moment . . . feel the tension in the muscles of your chest. . . . Let the air flow from your lungs naturally, and allow your shoulders and arms to relax."

I could feel the difference! I could feel how the tension felt in my lungs as I held my breath, tight, uncomfortable. And I felt the relief as I let the air out.

"Then once again on your own you can continue a few more times and as you do, sense the deep, regular rhythm of your breathing . . . sense a calm as you exhale. . . . As the air flows from your lungs, your shoulders and upper arms will follow, feeling loose and relaxed. . . . Again, sense the calm that comes from exhaling."

The entire exercise lasted twenty minutes, during which time he counted from twenty down to one. At each number I was to feel a growing sense of relaxation, each number representing a different part of my body. His voice was so easy to listen to. With each number, much to my amazement, I did feel a growing sense of relaxation. I wasn't quite sure why or how this was working, but it was working. My thoughts were completely centered around myself, telling my body to feel relaxed, and the most incredible part was that I actually felt more relaxed. For the first time in a great while I felt as if I had a some control over my body again.

Al had taped our session and told me there was a tape

recorder out at the nurses' station so that I could practice this exercise at least twice a day. I took the tape and thanked him, leaving the room in disbelief at what had just happened. But I did not practice. I remained unconvinced I could control even the slightest amount of pain through learning relaxation techniques. I thought it was nice while it lasted, but as soon as I stepped back onto 7-B, I buried what had happened in the back of my mind.

NOVEMBER 27, TUESDAY EVENING

The Clinic was my hideaway. As far as everyone back home was concerned, I was just in the hospital-no special place, no controlled environment, just in a regular room in the hospital. The only person outside of Scott and Deb who knew where I really was, was my dear friend and neighbor, Joanne. Other than those three people, I saw no need to tell anyone else, not even my parents. After four weeks there, I had not changed my mind about the psych ward: It was still something to be ashamed of, to keep well hidden from friends and family.

We were to some extent an experimental group, and new programs were always being added. That night was our first session with Dr. Sue Powers, who lead a group including spouses, where we discussed how pain affected our lives as families and how family members might relate to us once we were home. They, too, would have to learn to relate to us as people and not patients. The biggest problem was that we all lived so far away, none of the family members could attend. Tuesday night at six-thirty was impossible for Scott.

I returned to my room after dinner that evening. I had told Deb about the family group and said there was no reason she should visit tonight, knowing there was only about forty-five minutes before the family group got started.

Joan poked her head out of the nurses' station as I passed, her long hair falling away from her body as her head turned to the side, saying, "You have a visitor waiting in your room." I didn't give it too much thought, assuming it was probably

Deb, who had decided to visit after all if only for a few minutes. I continued walking toward my room looking forward to seeing Deb sitting there waiting for me.

My god! My father! How did he find me? How did he get in? What the hell is he doing here? My God. Oh my God!

I immediately panicked! I saw the bathroom door ajar next to me and darted in, my mind racing. I could feel my head burning, my body wet with sweat. My mind was spinning and I was shaking from head to toe. I had thought I was safe in the hospital, that no one would find me there. Who would want to! I was not prepared to deal with anyone at that point, especially not my father. I knew I couldn't handle his reaction, his disappointment in finding out where his daughter was. I had thought my secret was safe—that I was safe!

I tried to regain control of myself, tried to get up the courage to walk out there, all the while thinking of a reasonable explanation I could give my father for being on 7-B. The very same man I had been having such difficulty dealing with in my imagination was now here in person. He would be sure to think I had gone off the deep end, that I was really crazy. He was not a patient man, and I wasn't sure if he would give me a chance to explain or if he would get angry without waiting for an explanation. At that moment I felt as if I were about to face a total stranger, with a horror story that was sure to create a negative, violent reaction.

I had to face him. Could I? As I reached for the door knob, I could feel my heart racing, ready to leap out of my chest. My hand was wet with sweat as the door knob slipped without opening. Nervously I rubbed the palm of my hand on the side of my jeans, hoping the knob would obey my sweaty grip and open. It did. I took a deep breath, told myself I could face him, and walked out of the bathroom, slowly, cautiously.

It seemed as if I were now in slow motion as I approached him. Each step I took toward him felt as if I were walking through sand dunes. As I reached the other chair, my body turned around like a broken toy. Without saying a word I sat down, my eyes focused on the far wall, unable to even look his way.

After several moments of painful silence he picked up the brochure lying next to him on the table. As he flipped through the pages he said, "You will like Aruba. Your mother and I had a really nice time there. Make sure you take a camera." Scott had told my parents about his surprise trip. "It's a small island, but there are a lot of things to do there. You'll be able to try the slot machines." He chuckled, saying, "Your mother couldn't get those things to pay her anything."

Where was the anger? Didn't he realize where I was?

"When are you leaving?" he asked.

"Sometime after the holidays, I think." It was difficult for me to respond to his casual questions. I sat waiting for the bomb to go off at any minute. I expected him to quickly change his tone and begin to question me.

> *"You know your mother is going to die when she finds out that you lied to her. And you're in the ward with the crazy people! God, Penney, what the hell is wrong with you? Can't you do anything right? What in the world am I going to tell your mother?"*
>
> *"Tell her that her daughter has finally lived up to her expectations: less than adequate. I have finally lost it. I am finally being 'like that!' Tell her I am sorry."*

Once again I heard my father's voice. "That's a good time to leave. That is when we went."

When is he going to yell?

"I had a client here in Cleveland, so I thought I would see if I could find you." His voice sounded so sincere, no trace of anger in it.

"Oh." When was he going to confront me?

"How are you getting along here? Are they helping you at all?"

Is this it? Is this where he lets me have it?

"Yeah, I guess. It's hard." I looked at him. He appeared to be so calm. I had to get rid of him before he . . .

"What time is it?" I asked.

He pulled the cuff of his shirt away from his wristwatch and said, "Ten after six. Why, do you have somewhere to go?"

"I have a class in ten minutes. I guess we'll have to cut our visit short," I said slowly. My heart was in the pit of my stomach.

"Well, okay." He was willing to leave.

Why is he here? Did Dr. Covington send for him? When is he going to yell at me?

"I'll walk you to the elevator. My class is across the hall." I got up and walked towards the door. I wanted to escape him.

He followed me down the narrow hallway. He walked beside me, and when we got about halfway down the hall, he took my hand and he said, "Well, I'm glad to see you look so good. Your mother will be glad to hear that. You should give her a call."

Here it comes. Oh, the guilt.

"I don't have a phone in my room. It's hard to get the pay phone. I'll try, though." My tongue tripped over each word.

As we approached the end of the hall, I knew I would have to buzz in order to get off the ward, to have the door opened. I hoped I would be able to reach down and quickly press the button without him noticing. I honestly didn't think he realiz-

ed where I was. I immediately heard the buzz and opened
the door.

"What is that for?" He looked at me with a frown on his
face, forehead wrinkled, eyes narrowed.

"Oh, ummm . . . the security is pretty tight in the Clinic."
I honestly don't know where that reply came from so quickly.
Why didn't I just tell the truth? I was afraid. Afraid of him.
I just wanted him to go away and leave me alone.

I walked him to the elevator and stood waiting.

> Come on, come on, don't make me wait any more. Elevator,
> come on . . .

Once the doors of the elevator opened, my father turned
and gave me a kiss on my cheek, a gesture that was out of
character for him. Now the guilt I felt was even more intense.

"Take care of yourself," he said as the doors met.

I was in a state of shock. I couldn't think, I couldn't move.
I just stood looking blankly at the elevator doors as if in a
trance. My breathing was slow and shallow. I felt nothing. I
didn't want to feel anything. Lizzy broke my trance as she
placed her hand on my shoulder, saying, "What's wrong? Penney, you okay?"

I heard her but could not respond. My mind was replaying the first sight of him, my body still experiencing the
initial panic. Lizzy grabbed my arms and gave me a gentle
shake. "Penney! What the hell is wrong with you?"

"That was . . . my . . . my . . . father!"

"Oh, my God!" She took my hand. "Come on in here
and sit down. You look like you saw a damn ghost or
something."

As I sat in family group, surrounded by people, I didn't
really care about, I could feel my spirit sliding deep within
myself. I had no desire to talk to anyone. I sat in silence, afraid

and very confused. The shock I had felt when I first saw my father still rippled through my body.

> I thought I was safe here. I thought . . . God, I don't know what I thought. What did he want? Why did he come here? Here, of all places. He didn't even visit me the last time I was in the hospital in Pittsburgh. Why now? What did he want?

My mind became overwhelmed by questions. I needed to have answers, but I had no means of getting them. I could feel myself pulling quickly away from reality. I no longer cared to be a part of the world. Escape and horror were dominating my thoughts. I felt as if I were sinking into the chair beneath me, as if I were being swallowed up, slowly disappearing from view.

"Penney, who was that man you were with earlier?" Carol asked as she entered the room, drawing me slowly back to my surroundings, my body becoming painfully aware of the here and now.

I did not respond immediately, forcing Carol to ask her question again. Timidly I replied, "My father," but said nothing more. I no longer wanted to talk to them or to anyone. I needed time. I had no idea how I would deal with the situation. All I really knew was that both my mind and body were in shock, and it was painful.

That night family group was a complete waste of time. I had no idea what was going on during the meeting, nor did I care. I kept replaying the scene with my father. God, what would I do?

Recreational therapy was part of our daily routine, shared by all the patients on the ward. It was meant to be a time of relaxation and fun, and quite often it was just that.

Rod was the orderly who planned and took care of all the details of each night's activities. Every two weeks a different patient would work with him. It was my misfortune to be given this task for the next two weeks. I had planned, a week at a time, what we patients on 7-B would do to fill the hour each night from eight until nine.

True to form, I made up my mind that I would make it the best two weeks they ever had. I would prove to them just how capable and organized I was. I had to prove to them and to myself that I could still function.

This particular night was going to be a blockbuster. I figured with the holidays coming up we should make candy. At first I didn't think Rod would approve since we would have to bring in a hot plate to melt the chocolate, but even he was looking forward to this. Scott had put together all the things we would need—a half pound each of six different colors of chocolate, molds, brushes to accent the designs, wrappers, even boxes to put the candy in—and had brought them with him the previous weekend. I had been looking forward to it until my Father's visit. After that, I didn't care. When I got through with family group, all I wanted was to go to my room, shut the door, and be left alone.

Lizzy stopped by just before eight. "Penney, you feel like going through with this candy thing tonight?"

"I have to."

"No you don't. Everyone will understand."

"No. They're counting on me."

"I'll do it for you then. Just tell me what I have to do and I'll do it." Lizzy was serious. Then she added, "Lord help them all!"

Usually the pain group took no part in recreational therapy. They didn't feel obligated to please the staff by being there, nor did they care what the other patients thought. But that night, of all nights, everyone came to the lounge to help me out. Lizzy, Helen, Joyce, and Carol were all there, ready and willing to help me get through the ordeal. It was only their presence that allowed me to get through the ordeal. The time quickly passed and before I knew it, it was ten o'clock. Once they were gone and most of the mess cleaned up, I began again to replay the experience of just a few hours before. My control was fading; I knew I had to be alone.

NOVEMBER 28, WEDNESDAY

During group my thoughts were focused on my father's surprise visit and the devastating effects it had on me. Although I was in a room filled with people, I felt alone, the awful sense of dread continuing to gnaw at me. Sounds outside my head did not exist. The people in the room were only vague images, gray objects filling the chairs. I had placed myself in a time warp where no sound could be heard, no touch could be felt, no light could be seen. There I remained for almost an hour.

Then life became real again as I felt Dr. Covington's eyes burning through my skin. I knew he was looking at me, waiting for me to say something, but I was unwilling to acknowledge my presence in the room. I was still locked tightly in my own world. A silence descended over the group. All conversation stopped as Dr. Covington's eyes remained focused on me. The wall clock overhead was the only sound to be heard.

"Penney, I understand you had a visitor last night. Want to tell us what happened?" Dr. Covington asked, his words sounding like the boom of a canon as they cut through the silence.

"No. I can't. I need time to . . . to . . . no," my voice replied in a whisper as my words faded quickly in the hush of the morbid stillness.

"Time! How much time do you need? Your time has just about run out lady!" Dr. Covington yelled. His words reverberated in my head as panic overcame me. Anger instantly filled my being as my eyes remained fixed on the floor.

"What the hell do you think this is? Haven't you wasted enough time and money already? You damn well better start to face what you are! You have been feeling sorry for yourself long enough!'' A burning hate swelled within me, my face hot with anger. ''Why don't you get off it, quit pretending to be so damn fragile. You want everyone to think you are helpless.''

I'm not! I'm not! I'm strong, you bastard . . . strong!

''We both know you hate everyone in this room. Go ahead, tell them you hate them. Tell them to _____ off! Go ahead!'' He demanded.

Anger was so deep inside of me now that I forgot momentarily about the previous evening. There was no one to save me as his voice closed in on me.

''I'm going to give you to ten to tell everyone here to _____ off. I'm going to give you one chance or I'll send you home!''

You son of a bitch!

''One . . . two . . . three . . . .'' I could feel the rage building inside of me.

I don't want to go home, not yet. I'm not done yet. I have too much I don't understand. I still need this bastard who calls himself a doctor. He has taken me too far; he has uncovered too much. He can't give up on me now . . . the bastard!

''Four. You'd better start talking. Five . . .''
I could hear myself saying the words over and over in my mind, but I couldn't get those words past my lips—not here. But he continued to count. I felt as if he were counting my life away, taking away the only chance I had left. I had to stop him. For an instant I felt like slugging him, preventing his words from entering the dead air. Instead, his words grew louder and louder as my rage became more intense. I had to stop him!

Carol now joined in attacking me—the last person I would allow to verbally abuse me. "Come on Penney. Why are you playing games? We know you, you're a fake!" Quickly the others joined in, taunting me with "You're a fake," "You're gutless, let it out Miss Perfect." Everyone was pushing me too hard, it was too much.

"I HATE ALL OF YOU! _____ ... ... LEAVE ME ALONE! LEAVE . . . ME . . . ALONE!"

Tears filled my eyes. The room became a mass of blurry objects as the tears streamed down my face. I had never cried like that before. So many tears, I had no control over them. Tears, confusion, anger. The room became quiet once more. I felt strange as if I were in a dimension not familiar to me, in a place where rational thinking didn't exist, a place where I had finally lost all control of my emotions.

> I see the bright light. The light I first thought was the light of death . . . clear, free. Am I free? Was it my own repression of thoughts and emotions that always gave me the gray, somber feelings? The light—is it understanding? Is it freedom from oneself? Do a few words make me free? But . . . the air is fresh again. The peace I feel within is warm, real, comforting. I have finally learned how to walk. I took my first steps.

Dr. Covington knew exactly what he was doing. He wanted me to cry, to lose control. He wanted to get me back to the beginnings of my feelings so that I might begin to understand myself and see that emotions are merely natural reactions, put there so that we can attain realistic control. To do this I had to be honest with myself, allow myself to recognize my own feelings. My pain was a problem I had to deal with, a difficult one in itself. But keeping myself so uptight emotionally, so overcontrolled, was driving my pain past endurance. If I was to learn how to deal with my pain, I would have to begin by reducing the stress and the amount of effort it took me to remain in control. I was using every ounce of energy I had to fight off emotions, tears, and sometimes even laughter. I needed to express honest emotions, without all the restrictions I placed on them. Without that freedom of expression I would never have been able to deal with any feelings at all. It was my first step in accepting myself.

Once I regained my composure, I lifted my eyes and just looked at the group. I saw and understood how much they cared about me, regardless of what I might say. They allowed me to be me without any rules. Even Dr. Covington reassured me that I had taken a big step toward recovery. I knew he was feeling good by his confident stride as he walked out of the room that morning. Promising to see me later in the day, he said, "You'll be okay, turkey, you are going to be okay."

I have just been born. The chains of emotional torment have been removed. Today is the day that I start over again. I have just been born.

I would never have accepted the idea of 7-B had I not been so completely worn out by the pain I experienced. It had been suggested by a doctor in Pittsburgh that in order to deal with my pain, I might have to learn how to reduce stress in my life. He went so far as to propose that I seek professional counseling. He was not suggesting my pain was psychosomatic, but that was my interpretation. To me, going for psychological help meant that it was my own fault I was hurting, that there was be no physical problem, that I had created the pain in my body. Sort of self-punishment. That was the reason that I never gave myself the opportunity to go beyond conventional medical care before I came to the Clinic. I had always thought that it would be pills and physical therapy that would fix me up, not psychiatry. I knew my pain was entirely physical in origin, at least that is what I tried to tell myself. I took all the doctor's well-meaning advice and turned it into scorn for their opinions, when it was actually my own self-doubt, my inability to believe in myself, that prevented me from hearing what they had to say.

To set the record straight, I did, and still do, have a physical problem. But after my experienced at the Clinic, I realized that other factors played a big part in the amount of pain I felt. I had tried to keep my physical and emotional sides separate, believing that they were two entities in and of themselves. I was so busy running away from what I was feeling emotionally, and focusing only on my physical being, I became lost in the pain. Fear of rejection and weakness prevented me from being objective about proper medical treatment, a treatment that would have included psychological counseling.

After I had cried and lost control I couldn't believe how relaxed and soothed I felt. I recognized clearly for the first time the weight of my unresolved feelings and the tremendous strain they had put on my body.

True, all the exercise, the weight lifting, and even the medicine I had been taking helped reduce my pain. I could, after four weeks of strenuous work and exercise, say that my pain had decreased. Although pain was still very much a part of each day, some days were better than others. Moreover, I had begun to recognize my physical limitations and to realize how far I could push myself before I had to stop. I was beginning to feel confident that I would, in time, be able to go home and resume a relatively normal life, physically.

Now the insight I had gained that morning in group allowed me to see ways to alter my lifestyle for the better. There was still much I had to learn, much yet to discover about myself. But that morning I felt I had taken my biggest step in understanding myself. I may have been overconfident, but I needed to feel good.

Dr. Gabis was standing in the hall when I returned to the ward. He already knew what had happened in group that morning. As I passed him, he reached out a hand and touched my arm. A simple gesture. But to me his action was much more than a gesture. I looked directly at him, perhaps for the first time, my eyes meeting his with confidence. His smile was genuine as he said, ''Congratulations! I will be in to see you later on. Good work!" Tears of joy now filled my eyes as I walked back to my room, Dr. Gabis's smiling face still vivid in my mind's eye.

"So. How do you feel now? By your expression I would say that your feet haven't touched the ground since group this morning," Dr. Gabis said. It was late morning by the time he entered my room.

I just smiled and looked at him. I could actually feel the sparkle in my eyes. The world seemed covered with a silver cloud. There was no bad, no evil, no pain. I could be me, say whatever I felt at the time, and still be accepted. There was nothing wrong with me. I could be free without fear of judgment. I felt good inside for the first time in a long, long while.

"I don't want to burst your bubble, but you must realize that today was just a first step. You still have quite a bit of work ahead of you," Dr. Gabis explained to me. "Enjoy the feeling today, for tomorrow we go back to work." He looked directly at me, his expression one of pride.

I did not hear his caution. All I could feel was joy. The air was clean. The sun shone brightly outside my window. The room was filled with color I had not really noticed until then. The whole world was right with me.

Later that day Dr. Covington also came to see me. His expression was similar to Dr. Gabis's as he entered my room. Without waiting for him to settle into his chair, I eagerly began to explain my thoughts. "I always thought I had to be in control. I had to be strong. I was always the one people came to because of my strength, not because of weakness as you suggested. I had to remain in control, especially of anger, so that I would be accepted. I never really liked who I was, so I always looked to others to like me. I guess I figured if someone felt positive about me, perhaps I would begin to like myself." I paused for a moment, remembering . . .

"Sure I'll do it. No problem," I said to a friend of mine. She had asked me to watch her kids for the day so she could get her shopping done without them hanging all over her and asking for everything in the store. I had my own plans that day. I was having company for dinner that night and had quite a few things to prepare. But I was actually afraid to tell this woman no. I believed that if I was unwilling to help her out she would never talk to me again, that she would no longer be my friend. So I said yes. And spent the day regretting it. What I wanted was a friend, someone who would like me . . . so I could like me. As always, I allowed myself to be used. Thinking about it, most of my life had been spent doing for others only to see them turn their back on me as soon as I needed them. I was never really being true to myself.

"And how do you feel now?" he asked. My mind was still on the past. "Penney?"

"What?" I looked over at him. "I'm sorry, what did you say?"

"How do you feel about yourself now?"

"I'm not sure, but I think I won't be so hard on myself from now on. I know that I have feelings, and not all of them are nice ones." I cleared my throat and continued. "But after this morning, well, I think that maybe I don't always have to take the other guy into consideration first. I have a right to feel and think what I want. I have always been my own worst enemy. Maybe I just cared too much."

"I can vouch for that. You are about as hard on yourself as anyone I have come across. It's going to take some time to find the middle ground, but I think you're doing good, turkey."

"Life is really complicated isn't it? It really is," I said, answering my own question. "I'm going to try to be more normal from now on."

"Please! Whatever you do, don't be normal. There is really no such thing as 'normal.' What is normal for one surely isn't

normal for someone else. We have to set our rules in accord-
ance with our value judgments. Hell, there are a lot of times
I like being abnormal, letting go for a while. I think normal
for you is maintaining control of your emotions. I would go
crazy if I tried to remain in control all of the time. God! No
wonder you were so down.

"Yes, but I always felt as if my worth was determined by
my actions. I mean, there are certain rules that society—and
parents—place on each of us. You know, the rights and
wrongs. If I stepped outside of those guidelines, I would be
reprimanded, punished. I believed I had to stay inside those
boundaries. Does that make any sense to you? Do you understand what I am trying to tell you?" I knew what I felt, but
had difficulty putting it into words.

"Penney, the only thing you are responsible for is your
actions, not your feelings. You are not responsible for what
you feel, only the actions you choose to take in response to
those feelings. Let me give you an example. Say you are driving your car down the road. You get pulled over by the state
police, who tells you that you were speeding. Your first thought
is I would like to give this guy a swift kick in the pants. That
is what you are feeling, but instead you politely give him your
license and say you'll be more cautious next time." He stopped
to look at me for a minute, turning his hands in an upward
motion, shrugging his shoulders. "Can you understand that?"

"Yeah. But it seems almost too simple. Feelings are internal, safe, free. Right?"

"Yes."

"And my actions are all that I am truly responsible for?"
I looked to him for conformation.

"Yes."

"So really, I still have to watch my actions? But, at least
I can feel whatever. That make a lot of sense." . . . *I think* . . .

"What you have to learn to do is be less controlling of
yourself. Allow yourself to react. This is only the first step for
you today. But I believe that losing the control you struggled

so hard to maintain is going to help you work through some of the other garbage you are still struggling with. We'll just take it one step at a time." He stopped a moment, looked directly at me as if he were trying to read my mind, then added, "You were a hard nut to crack!"

As Dr. Covington got up and left the room, I promised myself I was now going to think twice before I allowed the unwritten rules of society—and my parents—to determine what and how I should feel. I was determined to be free.

NOVEMBER 29, THURSDAY

Between what had happened in group the previous day and what I experienced in assertiveness training the next afternoon, I began to look at my pain from another angle. Was it possible that because of my inability to say no, I let my pain supply the excuse, an easy out from a situation I was not capable of dealing with. Did I do that?

Cheryl, an attractive, well-dressed young nurse with smooth ebony skin sat directly across from me as she said, "The majority of pain patients are notorious 'yes' people. They seem to be, for the most part, victims of friends and families. What we have found in working with pain patients is that more times than not they will simply say that they don't feel good, the pain is too bad, rather than say no. It is difficult for them to take the responsibility for their actions when their pain provides such an easy excuse. Now I'm not saying that any of you do that. But it is important that you become aware of how easy it is to allow your pain to be a universal excuse."

I listened intently as she spoke. I knew what she was saying. Her words seemed to mirror my life since my own pain had begun. "No" would have jeopardized the image I struggled to maintain: the nice gal who was always willing to lend a helping hand, the person who was always there when the chips were down, the someone to turn to when people needed to hear "yes."

"Now you have become victims of your pain, and your friends and families have become your victims to some extent. I'll bet most of you did not take on any responsibility, say six months or so before you came on this unit. It is easier to beg out of whatever because you hurt." As Cheryl explained the relationship of nonparticipation and our assumed inability, I gave her my complete attention. "No one ever questioned your unwillingness to become involved. Who would? You guys had a good excuse. Right?"

"Yes, I guess we did," Joyce's tiny voice replied. "I couldn't keep up with my family. They understood."

"Yes. But what did you tell them?" Cheryl asked.

"What do you mean? I told them I didn't feel good. I didn't! They understood."

"But was it because you didn't feel good or was it because they were requesting something of you that you did not want to do?" Cheryl was more penetrating than she had been in the past as she tried to make a point. "Why couldn't you just say no? Why did you allow your pain to take the responsibility for your actions?"

"I didn't." Joyce sat quietly for a moment, her mind drifting back to a time very familiar to her. "I don't like to go to the in-laws every Sunday. I hate doing that. Ever since we were first married, we had to go over there for Sunday dinner. Even when I became ill, I had to go to the in-laws."

"Why couldn't you just tell your husband that you didn't want to go?" Cheryl asked.

"You don't know my husband. There is only one way to do things. Only one right way—and that is his way."

As Joyce explained to Cheryl why she had to go to her in-laws, I began to think about the months before I came to the Clinic. I was hearing Joyce say that the only way to get out of doing something unpleasant was to use her illness as an excuse. Had I, had all of us, learned to use our pain to our own advantage? Was there some benefit to our suffering? Had my mind become that distorted over the years of suffering?

Although it was difficult to accept, I couldn't help but think that I did use my pain. The idea disgusted me. How could I have been so insensitive to myself and others not to recognize what I was doing? I began to think of small incidents where I had used my pain to some advantage. People aren't expected to be completely in control when they're in pain. No one thought twice about my lack of participation. I had a good excuse: I had pain.

I was only now beginning to realize how I had used my pain. It was a very hard thing to accept, but I now had to face some truths about myself. That is what I was doing at the Clinic. I had to gain a better understanding of myself. I could not leave one stone unturned if I was to get all that I could out of the experience.

Cheryl and Joyce continued their discussion on the ability to say no. I withdrew into my own world again. My mood began to swing from positive to negative as I began to see myself not only as the victim but as one who victimized others. The solid ground I had stood on for almost twenty-four hours began to break apart. Little pieces fell away as I returned to my self-criticism, rebuilding the same defenses that had restricted my actions and emotions. I began to raise my guard again, to watch out for unacceptable behavior, to recognize that I indeed had a bad attitude about most things. This time, however, I went in the other direction. I was not going to allow the slightest hint of pain to control me. So once more I began to overcontrol myself.

NOVEMBER 30, FRIDAY

For the three days following Suzy's departure, I had the room to myself. I liked having no intrusions while I gave myself up to questions running endlessly through my head. When

I needed company, there were the others in the group that I could go to. I saw my time alone as a good opportunity to reflect and speculate.

Friday afternoon all that changed. I was informed by Stella that I had the good fortune of getting a nice woman as my new roommate. Stella assured me that even though she was a psychiatric patient, once she got her medicine straightened out, she would be a sweet, pleasant person.

Bull! I didn't want a psych patient as a roommate, but like it or not, there she was. She must have recently lost a great deal of weight, for as she paced, she held tightly to the side of her slacks, trying to keep them from falling down, and her blouse hung from her shoulders. The sleeves came halfway down over her hands. Her deep, dark, glassy eyes moved rapidly from side to side as she shuffled along the floor, making me uneasy.

My first reaction was apprehension. She was crazy! I had no idea what she was capable of doing, and I didn't want to find out, either. She would have to go. I could not have someone so unstable complicate my progress. I was unwilling to understand or be patient with her. Although I had feared the rejection and unfair judgment of others to my being in the Clinic, I promptly behaved that way toward her. I judged her. I did not consider anything but what I saw before me: not a person, but a being with problems far too great to be successfully dealt with. I became angry that they would expose me to such an uncontrollable person.

I was infuriated by her presence. She didn't sleep at night, but continued her relentless pacing back and forth, mumbling with each unsteady step. It was several days before they moved her to another room, at which point she lost all control and went after her roommate, physically attacking her, and waking the entire ward with the noise. It took three staff members and ten minutes to pull the two women apart and restore peace. I thought, That could have been me she attacked! That could have been me! Safe indeed!

It wasn't until just before I left the Clinic that I gained a greater understanding of her and others like her. She was suffering from an illness she did not choose to have, an illness that was a constant torment and that made her an outcast to society. All she needed was understanding and compassion, which were such vital components in helping her prevail over her affliction. All she needed was understanding and direction.

DECEMBER 1, SATURDAY MORNING

Joyce was an easygoing person for the most part. She had gotten little relief from her pain, located in her face, and she periodically went to one of the dentists for treatments. Nonetheless, Joyce's time at the Clinic had given her a better outlook on life. She had gained some insight into her own needs and the right to have those needs met. Because of the role playing in assertiveness training, Joyce turned into quite a different person—more verbal, more forceful, and better able to make her needs known. It was easy for her, during role playing, to tell her husband that she didn't want to spend every weekend visiting the relatives. "No!" she shouted. Even though she was told to say no, not to give in, she was so convincing during the exercise that I felt certain she would have no trouble maintaining her assertiveness in a real-life situation and be free to become the person she wanted to be.

It was a cold December morning. I stood looking out of my window at the light snow covering the ground beneath. The tiny snowflakes seemed to glide from the sky. Small crystals collecting on the window ledge, each flake gently hiding the one beneath it. My mind was momentarily free from worry. The newness of the snow gave me a sense of hope.

"Penney, how are you?" A familiar voice cut through the silence of the room.

"Oh, Scott, I'm sorry. I didn't hear you come in. How are you?" My voice did not sound as sincere as I would have liked. "Did you have any trouble driving up? I'm glad to see you."

"I left early this morning. The roads were fine. What's been happening with you?"

I gave a quick I'm fine, answer and we headed back to the lounge for group, hand in hand.

Joyce and her husband, Fred were already there when we walked in. We took a few moments for introductions, none of us had met Fred, this was his first time attending a group. The subsequent conversation was awkward and strained. Soon the others joined us, and Dr. Covington began by saying, "I'm glad to see that some of the husbands are here. It's important that they understand what has taken place here so they will know how to deal with their wives once they return home."

Dr. Covington looked directly at Joyce as he asked, "Joyce, are you looking forward to returning home?"

"Yes." Her voice much softer than usual. I looked at her in surprise. She had been so up just last night about how much she wanted to get home and begin her new life. She had been so strong the previous night.

Now she sat quietly. Her expression was tight. Her forehead was wrinkled, her expression sad. Her eyes gazed off into a distant place that only she knew. It was as if some one had drained her of all hope. Why was she so . . . so different all a sudden?

"Fred, how do you feel about Joyce returning home? Can you tell us?" Dr. Covington asked, as his eyes remained on Joyce also.

"We are so anxious to have Joyce home with us again. We've missed her cooking. My son and I have eaten out most nights. I can't seem to make heads or tails of that dumb kitchen. It will be good to have her do what she did before she got sick. A woman's place is in the home, and that is where Joyce is the happiest. Isn't that right honey?" Fred looked to Joyce for verification.

Joyce, don't let him do this to you. Tell him all your plans.
Tell him you are going to be free.

Fred was a small man, not more than five feet six inches.
He still had a full head of hair, although it had turned a silver
gray over the years. He had an air of confidence about him,
yet his expression appeared to be meek. I would have thought
Joyce and Fred the ideal couple if it were not for his domineer-
ing attitude toward her.

"Yes, I'm anxious to get home so I can take care of my
family again." Joyce was contradicting everything she had been
saying about the changes she would make in her life, things
she was finally going to do for herself. What had happened
to the spunk she had exhibited recently? Why was she so willing to fall back into a position of a puppet? Why?

Within five minutes, in the presence of her husband, she
had surrendered. I had a strong urge to tell her husband to
go to hell, but of course I didn't. I just sat there, my blood
boiling, and listened to Fred plan Joyce's life for her. Because
of her, I actually believed we all had a chance to challenge
our tomorrows. She could choose freely when she was away
from her husband, but one look at him and she was once again
putty in his hands.

I was angry at Joyce. I was screaming inside, but I didn't
have the nerve to express my feelings. I was as easily manipulated as Joyce. I hadn't won anything either. We may all have
won one or two pretend battles, but the real war could never
be won. Both Joyce and I were too weak to have faith in
ourselves and stand up for what we believed.

DECEMBER 1, SATURDAY EVENING

Angered by what had happened in group that morning,
I lost my sense of freedom. I felt restricted once again by

distorted, half-truths that I tried unsuccessfully to ignore. Why didn't Joyce speak up? Why didn't I speak up? Why, for that matter did Carol, Helen, and even Lizzy sit quietly by while Fred dictated the path Joyce's life would follow?

To make things even more confusing, Joyce once again changed her tune that evening. The Cleveland winter had finally arrived with the temperature dropping thirty degrees in the past two weeks. Everyone but Lizzy had arrived at the Clinic in lightweight coats. But with the onset of the winter weather, we had all requested our families to bring our heavy coats so we would not freeze while out on pass. And we had all received them, except for Joyce.

Joyce did not say too much as she left the Clinic with her husband in the afternoon, but when she returned that night, cold and tired, she again became verbally aggressive. "He can't remember my coat, but he sure as hell didn't forget his damn bottle of booze! That man has about as much concern for me as a fly on the moon. All he ever does is sit around the damn house and drink his damn bottle of booze. Damn It! I froze my buns off out there today. Damn him!"

Joyce paced back and forth in her room as she continued. "You want to know something? You know what the son of a bitch did to me? He, that man I vowed to love and obey, got so damn drunk the night our youngest was born that I had to call a friend to take me to the hospital. I had to have the baby without the support of my husband!" By now Joyce was raging mad. "I can't begin to count the number of times he was not there when I needed him because he was off in some sleazy joint with his buddies drinking himself into oblivion."

"Joyce, settle down," Carol demanded in a firm tone. "You're going to blow a gasket, woman. Did you tell him how you felt? Does he know how upset you are?"

"Well . . . yes . . . in a way he does." Her voice was much softer as she answered.

"What is 'in a way'? You didn't say anything, did you?" Carol continued, not willing to let the subject rest.

"You don't understand. What would I do if he got mad at me? What would I do?" Joyce stopped in her tracks, looking directly at Carol. Her eyes full of alarm.

I had to ask, "What are you so afraid of Joyce? What can he do to you? You have a right to be mad."

"Yeah, I know that, but it's a lot easier to be assertive here when it's just pretense than when I am face to face with the real thing. He may look like a nice guy, but you don't know him like I do. He has a terrible temper. He . . . he . . ." Joyce fell silent.

No one spoke. The room was filled with people, but there wasn't a sound. We were all lost in our own thoughts.

Yes, pretending is easy; it's the real thing we're not yet able to face. How much have I really gained?

I left without further comment and went back to my room to think. I was frustrated by Joyce's interaction with her husband. I wondered if all of us were perhaps fighting a losing battle.

In the solitude of my room I reflected on the day, not only what had happened in group, but what had happened with Scott: I had hesitated to get really close to him. I became uneasy as I began to realize how uncomfortable I was talking openly about sex. Dr. Gabis had once called me a Pollyanna, and he may have been right. There were so many things about sex I didn't understand but had never asked. Why? Was I ignoring a problem and seeing only the bright side?

I tried hard to ignore such thoughts, but they made my attempt to read a book futile. I couldn't remember one word of what I had read. What made me zero in on sex now? God knows I had enough to deal with: What was I going to do with the rest of my life? What direction would I chose? Would I return home better than when I left? Those questions alone were more than I could handle, so why was I getting caught up in something as unimportant as sex?

Or was it? Did I really believe that or was that my way of avoiding it? God, how I hated 7-B late at night! There was far too much time to think about life, death, and even sex. How could I have forgotten the uneasy feelings I experienced with Scott? How could I go on ignoring the pain of sex? Pain, not overpowering, but enough to make me resistant to any sex at all. Pain I had forgotten about until today when Scott and I made love.

I began to examine all the possible causes. I tried to gain insight on my own into something I knew very little about. As a child I never received a clear explanation from my mother about why or how girls go through some bizarre thing they referred to as a period every month. I sensed she was uncomfortable with it and I picked up on it. None of the kids I knew in school ever approached the subject of sex without their own uneasy feelings reflected in what they said and how they said it. I picked up on their attitudes as well and assumed it was something that should not be discussed openly.

As a result, I knew very little about sex while I was growing up. I believed my eighth-grade girl friend when she told me a girl could get pregnant sitting on her boy friend's lap in shorts! It's hard to believe, but I think that until I was in training to be an X-ray technician, I did not really understand where babies came from. It was just a subject that I, and everyone around me, felt uncomfortable talking about.

So there I was, thirty-one years old and still not completely comfortable with sex. Although I certainly knew the biology, I was still ill at ease talking about sex, even with Scott. The pain I had experienced kept nagging at me. Why was it there? Were my feelings once again taking over? Was this another way my body had of dealing with uncomfortable situations?

At one time, I could have easily ignored such feelings by denying myself that anything was wrong. But I had come too far on the road of self-examination, and I had opened too many doors already to quit now. I knew that my life could be so much easier if only I understood and put into perspective the pieces of the puzzle. No, I could not forget sex. I had to talk about it. I had to understand why I was so ill at ease with it.

Joan was on duty that night. It was already ten o'clock, but I had to talk to someone then, before I lost my nerve. She had told me I could come to talk any time, no matter how late. I went out to the nurse's station and asked her, "Can we go somewhere and talk? That woman is still in my room and acting real strange tonight."

"Sure, let's go back to the music room. Just give me a minute to finish this form."

I stood out in the hall, my back against the wall, waiting until Joan appeared. I followed her back to a small room at the end of the hall. This room was usually empty. Only an old piano stood in the corner of the room. As she reached for the light switch she asked, "So what is it?"

"'I've been thinking. I. . . I need to talk to someone about this. It isn't a real big problem. At least I don't think so." I continued to beat around the bush until finally I said, "To-day . . . Scott and I were . . . were . . . making love. I, uh, wasn't real comfortable with it. That is to say, uh, I had some discomfort . . . have had it for a while."

I looked at her for a reaction. I saw nothing in her expression which indicated ridicule, so I asked, "Is it me? Is this pain a part of my problem? I mean . . . is it real? Or am I . . . you know?"

"How long have you been experiencing pain?" she asked.

"About six months I guess."

"Well, I can't determine what is causing the pain, but if you don't mind I'd like to talk with you about how you feel about sex. That is, if you don't mind. Are you comfortable with that?" Joan's voice so reassuring, so natural.

"I'll try." I looked away for a moment, again trying to find a place to begin. "I feel so dumb about the whole thing. I should know all this stuff by now."

"Not necessarily. It depends a great deal on what you've been exposed to in your lifetime. A lot of people have distorted and bizarre ideas about sex." Her face was serene and calm as she spoke. "Have you talked with Dr. Covington about any of this?"

"Are you kidding! I don't think I'm ready for that. He tries to bring the subject up in group, but somehow it always gets sidetracked. I think the entire group is afraid of the subject."

For the next hour Joan and I sat in the small room talking. She was so comfortable talking about sex that I automatically felt more at ease. She reassured me that with effort on both our parts, we would be able to talk more openly about our sex life. It would take time, but I knew I was willing to try.

When I returned to my room I began to think about what Joan had said and the attitude the entire group seemed to have about sex.

To Joyce, sex was just another duty a wife must perform. She thought that women were not meant to enjoy sex. It was certainly forbidden for a woman to want sex or to be so presumptuous as to be the initiator. Joyce used her strict Catholic upbringing to justify her beliefs. Even Dr. Covington was troubled by her view and suggested she and her husband seek out sex therapy. He offered to set up an appointment at the Clinic. "Absolutely not! You shouldn't talk about that kind of stuff. I will not do it. Just let me be! I've managed so far on my own!" Joyce said indignantly, her finger wrapped tightly around the cloth handkerchief she often carried with her. "I will not go, so don't ask me again. Why do I need that at my age anyway?"

Helen felt justified in not taking part in such discussion. She had never been married and thought that we assumed she'd never had sex. It was a naive assumption on her part. Perhaps she was too embarrassed to admit her own natural desires and actions. Helen was in her early seventies and she had been raised in a different time, when values were much more rigid than today.

Carol would not really talk about her relationship with her husband. She'd only say, "It's too painful for me to think about him. It's too painful to remember how wonderful we were together."

Lizzy, the most outspoken of all, would often write on her pain sheet "hot and horny" instead of the usual description of pain. As long as the discussion was about sex generally, with no personal experiences attached to it, Lizzy acted as if she were very well-adjusted sexually. Only a serious discussion of sex would make her pull back and fall into silence. She declined to answer questions about her greatest fear—being raped. For Lizzy it was a real fear; it had happened to her twice already, and the scars remained deep within her. Only once had she ever talked about the attacks in group, and even then she ran out of the room in tears before the discussion was over.

Sex is a natural part of life, an act of love between a man and a woman and the beginning of life itself. Why were we all so afraid of it? As my memory of those group sessions faded, I went to bed, tired, uncertain, but sure that at least one problem had been solved. Joan had provided me with as much help as I thought I needed.

DECEMBER 3, MONDAY

I listened intently as Carol and Lizzy talked of the unspoken words, misinterpreted gestures, and outright denial of feelings between themselves and their fathers. They had let the love that could have been, slip away. All the special moments that a daughter and father should share were gone, left undiscovered. Now it was too late. Too late to make up for lost time. Too late to say the things that they should have said. Both Carol's and Lizzy's fathers were dead.

Carol explained to the group, "You know that after my mother died, my dad put us all in a home. He said it was best for everyone. All my life I hated him for doing that to us. But I hated that home even more. It was a cruel and insensitive place. I thought that he didn't love us. What I didn't know then was that work was hard to come by. With six kids, he had to make enough money to feed and clothe all of us, and the only job he could get kept him on the road. It would have been impossible for him to give us any kind of supervision.''

Carol let out a deep sigh as she continued to explain, ''After my husband died I think that is when I really understood. God! It was impossible for me to be both mother and father to my kids. I loved them and I wanted them, but, if my husband had not left me as well off as he did, I don't know how I would have supported those children.''

Carol stopped for minute. A sad look came over her face as she stared off in the distance. ''It is too late for me now. My father is dead. For me it is too late to tell my father that I understand why he did what he did.'' Tears welled up in her eyes, her shoulders sagged, and she continued, ''All those years that I had only negative words for him. All that time that my heart was filled with resentment—and now . . . now he's gone. I'm not saying that there wasn't another way for him to deal with the problem, but he dealt with it the only way he knew how. I didn't even tell him when I got married. He never knew any of his grandchildren.''

''God! I know exactly what you're talking about Carol.'' Lizzy was speaking now. ''My father left when I was ten years old. He just up and walked out on the old lady. Left me and my sister too, without as much as a damn good-bye. Left us high and dry, without a dime. I hated him for that. Then there were the years of listening to my mother crying for the bastard to come back to her. During that time my mom had men coming and going, in and out all the time. Never knew who the hell I was gonna find when I got up in the morning. Sometimes they would stay just long enough to make me feel like maybe they would stick around. You know, the ones I thought were okay. But damn, no one ever seemed to be able to hang tough. Wasn't until I was 'bout eighteen that I got the notion to go lookin' for my old man. I don't know, somethin' inside of me made me do it. I had to tell the bastard off I guess. Anyway, I got a lead that he was out in Utah. When I called him some old lady answered. I told her what I wanted, told her who the hell I was. Nice lady!'' Lizzy stopped talking.

No one made any attempt to comment as Lizzy collected her thoughts. "He was . . . he had . . . the damned old man had died on me before I ever got a chance to talk to him . . . the fool! The woman, she told me what she could about him. Said my dad talked about us often. And she said that it was my mom who kicked him out. Said he tried to see us, but the old bitch kept callin' the police if he got near the house. It wasn't no house. It was a . . . a prison."

I wondered, if in a way, I was doing the same thing to my father. Was I leaving him out of my life because of a lack of understanding? Did his gruff exterior keep his innermost feelings hidden? Was he hiding from something I didn't understand? Had I misunderstood him? Had I judged him harshly? Did my mother's mention of his negative reactions scare me into believing he was a terrible person? Was I willing to try to understand him, or was I merely being affected by what had been said in group that morning?

"Penney, you know you have the chance to do something about your dad. He did come all the way to Cleveland to see you. He must think something of you to do that. Don't make the same mistake that Lizzy and I have. Give him a chance . . . now." Carol pleaded with me.

"She's right, you know. Someday it will sink into that thick head of yours that you've wasted time, time you can't get back. You better give some thought to what you want to do about your dad. There is something there worth saving, Penney. I know there is. But . . . you might have to make the first move," Lizzy added.

As I got up to walk out of group, tears of regret and sorrow filled my eyes. I knew I would have to try to give him a second chance. I would have to show in some way the same caring that he showed the night he went out of his way to visit me, the night I began my long journey back to the human race.

DECEMBER 4-6, TUESDAY-THURSDAY

Physically, I was improving every day. I felt certain that I'd be able to handle the pain once I returned home. What I couldn't handle was the fact that I was still there. If I was in more control of my pain, why was I still on 7-B? What was it that kept me there? I had taken some big steps in dealing with my pain. Even my attitude about feelings had changed as I saw how they could have a direct effect on my physical well-being. Dr. Covington had managed to break down one of the biggest obstacles that lay in my way, my own suppressed anger. He had helped put my anger center stage where even I could see it. After that morning in group, I thought the rest of my stay would be relaxed. I thought I just had to tie up a few loose ends. I must accept the effect my parents had on me thus far, deal with it, let it go, and look ahead to the future.

"So, how are you today?" Asked Dr. Gabis as he walked into my room. "What's new with you?"

I looked at him and wanted to blurt out all sorts of doubts that were beginning to surface again. I wanted to ask him how much longer I'd be here. I wanted to know when he and Dr. Covington would complete their overhaul on my mind and body. I had so much to ask, but instead I replied, "Oh . . . nothing. I'm fine," my voice hollow, lacking any color.

How long had I been here now? I couldn't remember. It felt like a lifetime. Three, four weeks? I knew that I had already stayed longer than I should have. My welcome was wearing thin, as my mother would say.

With a great deal of apprehension in my words, I asked, "When do you think I can go home? I've been here an awful long time.

Haven't I?

"Do you think you're ready to go home?"

"God . . . I guess I am. I've been here a . . . long time. Don't you think I have?" Turning the conversation back to him, hoping he would just give me an out-and-out answer.

"It doesn't really matter what I think. What matters is how you feel." He sat with an air of confidence about him. Why couldn't I have been so . . . so . . . intelligent and confident. He knew where he was going. Dr. Gabis was at that very moment working toward his goal. To know exactly what you want must be wonderful.

"How do I feel?" I thought a moment. "I guess that would depend on when you asked me. Right now I'm not sure. I feel a little confused."

"Confused about what?"

"I don't know. I'm not sure what I want to do with the rest of my life any more. I'm not even sure what I want to do with the next week of my life right now."

"Then I suggest you answer that question first, before we talk about you going home. Think about it for a while. When you have the answer, then we'll talk about you going home." Dr. Gabis was so calm as he placed an enormous weight on me.

What do I want to do when I grow up? When do I know that I have grown up? What . . . what . . . what is the answer?

He wanted answers that I didn't have. I could have lied to him, told him that I was going to . . . what? I could not even come up with a good lie to tell him.

I took Dr. Gabis's question much too seriously. I thought I had to have a definite plan before I took one step out the door. I could not see the forest for the trees.

Time became irrelevant again. I was caught in hours of abstract deliberation of what would be and what once was. I assumed the worst about myself. I was lost in a hodgepodge maze of insinuations and misinterpretations, which swam around inside my head. Bewilderment clung to my every thought. I did not know which way to turn, or whether to put a halt to the madness.

Several days passed unnoticed. I was at a complete standstill in my thoughts. I reverted to my old ways of repressing feelings and pretending that nothing bothered me. Feelings of disappointment and frustration built up inside me as I once more convinced myself that I was unloved, and more important, unwanted. And I was unable or unwilling to put an end to these thoughts. I became apathetic toward the other members of the group. I was resentful of anyone I saw as able yet unwilling to help themselves. Suddenly the other group members' problems seemed trivial and unimportant. My own confusion and frustration consumed me. Once again I was convinced I was beyond help.

I could no longer hide. It was obvious to everyone who saw me that something was wrong. They saw my dejected expression, my eyes empty of all emotion. They repeatedly asked me what was wrong, and got an "I'm fine" answer. In that lonely, solemn place—my own thoughts—I withdrew even further into defeat and rejection.

"Penney, why don't you lighten up?" Lizzy said as we walked back from our afternoon PT. "I know something is wrong with you. What is it? Can I help?"

"No," I said without feeling. I kept my eyes straight ahead. Even though the halls were filled with people, I saw no one.

"Don't give me that crap. I know you well enough by now to know that something is eatin' you. Come on, spit it out." Lizzy's concern was in vain.

"Just . . . let me be," I quietly replied.

I was again in a deep depression, preferring to be alone in my room to ponder all that I had been through. It didn't seem possible that anything in my life, or in me for that matter, would ever really change. It seemed that so far all attempts at trying to change me had gone amiss. I knew words were just that, words. No one on 7-B had the ability to remake me into a . . . a . . . whatever it was they wanted me to become.

My feelings of being unloved and unwanted swelled deep within my very soul. Why do people love? And how do you know when you are loved? Is love what I have been looking for all this time?

I could not erase the hurtful words reverberating in my thoughts. Where was the switch to turn off my mind? I didn't want to think at all, it was far too menacing. Could I run away? Where would I go? But it didn't matter where I went, I would still be who I am. I would still be incomplete. If I could not love myself, how could I love another? Why couldn't I turn off my mind and start at the beginning again?

The golden rule said, "Do unto others as you would have them do unto you."—a phrase I had heard many times as a child, a phrase that had become a part of me. I always put myself in another's place when making the decision to react. How would I feel if someone did that to me, or said that to me? The answer usually was that I wouldn't like it. Thus, I became a people pleaser, one who was determined not to make others feel bad, or hurt them, or make them feel unimportant. But I did it at my own expense. Now I wondered if I had not treated my relationship with Scott in the same way. Had I, in the past, always allowed him to do things his way in order not to hurt him, to avoid making him feel bad? And, was I paying for that attitude now? Had I allowed Scott to be more important in my life than myself? Was our relationship one of love or accommodation? What was true love anyway? Is it not a forty-sixty relationship, each one giving sixty and only receiving forty? Did I get the positive feedback from Scott? Or . . . it hurt too much to think about.

I sat alone in my room, now in a great deal of pain. A deep ache in my arms forced me to remain still, and my head felt as if a hammer was pounding relentlessly on my brain. The gray, dreary light from the window intensified the pain in my head. I felt like the tin man in *The Wizard of Oz*, all rusty and stiff and unable to move. So I sat in my room alone and afraid, waiting for someone to come and take away the hurt. My desire to help myself had vanished. If I was to be helped, someone else would have to do it.

But who? Others had tried. Cheryl tried to cheer me up that afternoon by telling me I was being too hard on myself. She said that I had much more than I gave myself credit for. I didn't believe her. There was something missing in what she said. Something else was needed to make me believe that what she said was true. Maybe I saw her as merely doing her job, rather than being sincerely interested in my welfare. Maybe what was missing was the quiet, caring way that Dr. Gabis had of talking to me.

The room was only dimly lit by light filtering in from the setting sun when I heard him say, "I hear you're a little low today." His voice was soft and gentle.

Without looking at him, I replied, "Yes."

"Want to talk about it?"

I turned my eyes down toward the floor as I considered his offer. Silence engulfed the room for more than five minutes before I began. "I don't know. Life is just too hard. Too many people to please and not enough energy."

"What do you mean?"

"I'm not sure. All I know is that I don't have the energy to be all those things others want me to be. I can't go on like this. I can't be all things to all people." My voice trailed off.

After a moment Dr. Gabis asked, "Who said you had to be all things to all people?"

"I don't know. Isn't that the way life is? Don't people have to earn the respect of others? Don't I have to consider the other guy first? You know the golden rule, 'Do unto others as you would have them do unto you.' I want people to be nice to me, to care about me. So I have to be nice to them. I have to care about their feelings first. Don't I? But, somehow . . . my feelings seem to get lost in all of that. I mean, after a while it seems like people know that you are a patsy, and they begin to use you. 'Nice guys finish last.' Why can't I be important? Why aren't my feelings important to anyone?"

"They are."

"No, I don't think so. I feel used. I feel angry with the entire world right now. I feel . . . too tired to fight it any more. Some of us are important and some of us aren't. It takes too much energy to earn respect."

"Each and every one of us deserves the same respect. You don't have to buy it. And I don't think anyone should demand respect either. We are all the same. Each of us is special in our own ways." His voice was soothing, his words sincere, his concern genuine.

"All I want to do is be me. Just go through life being who I am, not trying to be what everyone wants me to be. Am I really that bad a person? I mean, other people don't have to work so damn hard to be liked; it just seems to happen for them. Why is life so hard? And I wasn't allowed to get mad, or I would be just like my father! I didn't use my illness. I remember when I was a kid, if I ever got sick, boy, my sisters would be right there telling me that I was faking. They said I was just trying to get out of doing my work. God! They never did any work. They were just mad because they would have to help out for a few days." Thoughts started coming to me. Angry thoughts. "You know, if I sat down for any length of time when work needed to be done, one of my sisters would always accuse me of being lazy! Can you imagine! She didn't do a damn thing, but I wasn't allowed to sit down—I was lazy! I have worked hard all my life just so people wouldn't think I was lazy.

Dr. Gabis just listened to what I said, and picked up on what I left unsaid. I could sense he really cared.

"I just want to be me . . . with no strings." I said.

"You know, a lot of what you experience as a child lingers in your subconscious. Between the ages of three and five everything your parents tell you, you believe to be undisputed fact. Even in adult life that part of you still remains, often confusing real issues. When you get two different sets of values, confusion is bound to follow. You have to become strong enough as an adult to overcome those ideas. You have to live your life the way you feel is best for you. You have to be the one responsible for your actions.

Dr. Gabis helped me to understand the difference between childhood values and adult values. It made sense to me. My mother's denial of negative emotions and my father's overuse of them had been tugging at me all my life. My one big problem was that I was not strong enough as an adult to separate truth from what I felt. I was trying to live up to two completely different values. One, anger was bad, and the other, anger was acceptable.

I understood enough of what he told me to rid myself of some of the guilt I had about my parents, never really knowing what mood they were in or how to react to them. It was their inconsistency about many things that often made me unsure about whether or not they were serious. Another dilemma I faced was not knowing whom to listen to, because they often disagreed. One parent would say playing cards is bad, the devil's doing, while the other would enjoy a weekly game of gin. The result was that on the one hand I knew cards were bad, but on the other I also knew it could be fun and acceptable, at least to one of my parents.

Dr. Gabis helped me to understand where some of my confusion was coming from. Perhaps there was an end to it.

DECEMBER 7, FRIDAY MORNING

December seventh was Carol's youngest child's sixteenth birthday, and she was determined to return home before the end of the day. She wanted to be there to see her daughter turn that magical age of sixteen. She could now stand on her own two feet and planned to finish college. Carol seemed to knew exactly what she wanted out of life, and she had no hesitation about leaving 7-B. The anticipation was evident on her face.

Carol's fear of her pain was gone, and although she was certain she could continue to improve and control her destiny, I was afraid for her. Would she be able to maintain her wellness once outside these walls? Or would she slip back into old habits? That was one question I did not even want to think about.

DECEMBER 7, FRIDAY AFTERNOON

"So, now there are four of you left. How do you feel about Carol leaving the unit?" Dr. Covington ask as he made his end-of-the-week rounds.

"Okay, I guess. She was ready to go. She is better." I said.

"Do you think you're better?" he asked as he lit a cigarette, the smoke dancing lazily up to the ceiling.

"I don't know. It depends when you ask me. Sometimes I would say yes, other times I would have to say no." I could hear the self-doubt in my voice.

Dr. Covington remained quiet for a moment before saying, "I talked with Joan this morning. She told me about a talk that you and she had a few days ago. I think you know what it was about."

For a moment my mind quickly went over the past few days. What had I said to Joan? Oh no! I remember . . . sex. She didn't . . . she wouldn't. In my own defense, or perhaps out of fear, I said, "I'm not sure." I hoped I had been wrong.

"Let me refresh your memory." He explained what I had said to Joan: that I had had pain during intercourse. He talked about my lack of understanding of sex. But he was considerate, and his words did not frighten me. I didn't feel as if I was dealing with some forbidden subject. His relaxed manner somehow made it easy for me to talk about.

"Yeah. I did talk to her about that. I was a little confused . . . that's all."

"Well, I think we need to talk about this. Are you game?"

"I guess." I hoped I would not show the embarrassment I felt deep inside.

"I think the first thing we need to do is get a complete sex history on you. Has anyone ever done that?"

"No. No one has ever done that." And I wished no one would now, I thought.

Dr. Covington was very direct in his questions. He wanted to know when I started my period. He asked if I had had premarital sex or any miscarriages. He questioned me about sexual feelings, if I masturbated, if I had orgasm with Scott, if I enjoyed sex. His questions were nonstop for about fifteen minutes and I tried my best to remain calm.

"I think we should have you examined while you're here, see if there's any physical reason why you're having pain. When did you have your last pelvic exam?"

"I'm not sure. I think it's been a while," I replied, dreading the thought of an exam.

"I'll have Stella set one up for you as soon as possible," he said as he wrote the order down in my chart. "Once that's done, I think we have to begin to focus on your attitude toward sex. I get the feeling that you are really uncomfortable talking about something that is a natural act, a basic need of every human, and one that should not be regarded as ugly or dirty."

I could not look at him as he continued to talk; I was too embarrassed. "I assume that you've said nothing to Scott about this pain that you experience, have you?"

"No."

"Can you and Scott talk openly about sex at all? I mean, do you tell him what you like, what makes you feel good?"

I remembered Joyce saying, "Women aren't supposed to enjoy it, they are just to do it." Now, faced with these questions, I realized I too felt the same way. "No. I guess I don't tell Scott what I like. I never thought I should. It might make him feel . . . inadequate. Wouldn't it?" I threw the conversation back to him.

He chuckled as he said, "He can't read your mind. To have a really good sex relationship you both have to communicate your desires to each other. There is nothing wrong with that. Why go through the motions if it is not enjoyable? I think that both of you need to be more open about your physical feelings for one another. If the exam comes up normal, I would like to schedule a session with a sex therapist here at the Clinic before you leave. I believe that you could benefit. You are indeed someone who has a lot of love to give. I think that you would be cheating yourself and Scott if you did not get a better understanding of your needs. What do you think?''

Right. I'll tell Scott that besides being physically and emotionally screwed up I am also a sexual mess. He'll love that!

I replied, with some doubt in my voice, ''I guess it won't hurt, if Scott is agreeable.''

''Okay turkey. I'll check back with you on Monday about it. Talk it over with him this weekend.'' He closed my chart and walked out the door.

DECEMBER 7, FRIDAY EVENING

Helen walked into my room, and without saying a word, sat down near the window. She seemed out of touch, as if she was in some sort of trance. She sat very still, her hands folded neatly on her lap, staring into space. Something was on her mind. I thought perhaps there was something wrong with her.

''You okay Helen?'' I asked.

''Oh yes. I was just thinking.''

''What about?'' I asked, a little worried by the distant tone in her voice.

''I don't understand why you're here. You look good to me. You have a nice husband, two lovely children, and the way you talk about your home, I would think you had everything anyone could want.'' Helen spoke honestly about how she saw me. She asked me right out what the hell I was doing there.

I had no answer for her. It was the same question I had been asking myself since the first day. But, what right did *she* have to ask me that? Helen, of all people, should have understood that things are not always as they seem. So I looked healthy! That is one of the most difficult aspects of chronic pain—there are no outward signs of it. Helen should have understood how drastically pain affects our lives.

"You are all aware of how important it is for your family to get involved in the program. I talked to each one of your families when you were admitted and thoroughly explained what was expected of them during your stay. I don't know how you can expect to go home and deal with anything if your family doesn't even care enough to attend these family sessions!" It was easy to see by the anger in her voice that she was very upset. Not one family member had showed up for the family group that evening.

I looked at Dr. Powers. Her small angular jaw was firm, determined. She scanned the room, her eyes stopping at each of us as if to ask, "What is your excuse this time?"

As my eyes met hers I had a sudden urge to explain Scott's absence, and without stopping to think, I said, "Scott does care. He is here every weekend. It is just really hard for him to get here on weeknights. I know that he would be here if he could. He would!"

Did she believe me? Was it acceptable for me to excuse Scott from these meetings because he had other obligations? Didn't everyone? Did I really believe what I had just told her? Or was I, too, doubtful of Scott?

The entire time I spent in group that night was focused on how I was going to prove once and for all how much Scott cared for me. When I returned to the ward I asked permission to go downstairs to make a phone call.

I knew that Scott would be at his parents' home that evening. "Hi. Is Scott still there, please?" I purposely avoided conversation with Scott's sister, who answered the phone.

As I waited for Scott to come to the phone, I turned to look at the large wall of windows to my left. The lights of the Clinic revealed a scene of wintry beauty as large snow flakes drifted past the window. It had been snowing heavily for almost an hour now.

"Hello." Scott's voice was at the other end.

"Scott. I'm so glad you're there. I have something to ask you."

"Is everything all right? Has something happened?" There was concern in his voice.

"No. Everything is okay. I just need you . . . I need you to be here for tomorrow morning." My thoughts were all focused on my immediate need: proof of Scott's loyalty to me. "They have been a little upset that you haven't made too many groups. Can you come?"

"Of course I'll be there. I just got to my mother's. Give me a few minutes and I'll leave. Call Deb and tell her I'm coming in tonight. I should get there around eleven. Okay kiddo. Hey . . . I love you." There was not the slightest hesitation in his voice. I needed him and he would come.

"Yeah, me too." I placed the phone back on the hook and called Deb to let her know that Scott would be in that night.

"Penney, why is he coming up tonight? The roads are really bad! He's going to have a tough time driving." There was a slight pause before she continued, "God, I hope he doesn't have any trouble."

Silence was all I could offer at that point. I knew what Deb was saying. I could feel the guilt building up, but I was out of control. I chose not to think about it. I would just forget about his driving up for now. He would be all right.

DECEMBER 8, SATURDAY MORNING

"Scott! You made it okay!" I walked toward him as he entered my room. "Did you have any trouble driving up?"

"Well, it wasn't the best ride I ever had."

"I'm sorry. It's just . . . we'd better go back to the lounge for group." I took his hand and led him down the hall toward the lounge.

Without saying anything, I walked over to the coffee pot and fixed Scott and myself a cup. He seemed different to me somehow. It was something I saw in his eyes, or rather what I didn't see in his eyes. He looked sad. Something was wrong!

I sat down beside him and reached for his hand. As my fingers touched his, the warmth of his skin made me aware of how cold my hand really was. His fingers grasped my hand gently, his grip tender. But he did not say a word.

"Scott, is something wrong?" He faced me as I spoke. "You don't seem like yourself. What is it? Tell me . . . please," I begged him, afraid that something tragic had happened.

"Penney . . ." His eyes were bathed in tears. He inhaled deeply, trying to gain control of his quivering voice.

The kids! Something must have happened to one of the kids!

"My mother called last night right after I got to Deb's. She . . . she . . . told me . . . my grandfather—he died."

My heart felt as if it had just stopped as I heard Scott say those words.

God! I made him come up here. How could I have done that?

There was absolutely nothing I could say to him to take away the grief he was feeling. I could not express my regret and guilt. Why had I made him come? Why was I so selfish?

"Are you okay? When did this happen? Scott, I'm sorry!" I knew nothing I said would help him. I was trying to hold back the tears. "Scott—I'm so sorry!"

"I know. I know. We all knew it was just a matter of time. But it still doesn't make it easy. It's going to be hard on my mother." A small tear rolled down Scott's face as he looked blankly into space.

The guilt I felt for insisting he come to Cleveland the previous night gnawed away at me as each painful second of group passed. Scott and I remained silent throughout group, each of us in our own world—his, one of sorrow, mine one of guilt and disgust for myself.

"Penney, you and Scott have been very quiet this morning. Is there something you would like to share with the group?" Stella asked, her voice reflecting her concern.

"What? Oh. Scott told me some bad news." I looked around the room at all the faces. Would they really care if I told them? What did it matter? "Scott's grandfather died last night." No feeling at all in my voice now.

"I'm sorry to hear that. Is there anything I can do?" Stella asked.

What could she do? What could anyone do? I had screwed up the whole thing. I was the one who felt the need to prove Scott's loyalty at all cost. What about his loyalty to his family? I hated myself at that moment. He should have been at home with his mother—with his grandfather!

Once group was over, Scott and I left the room. We needed to be alone, to talk. We headed back to my room. The atmosphere of the ward seemed somehow gray, saddened, as if there were some cloud of grief hanging over us.

I took Scott's hand and stood facing him in the middle of the room, avoiding his eyes. "Scott, you have to go home. You can't stay here now. You have to go," I pleaded with him.

He placed his hands on my shoulders, looked directly at me, and said, "No. I'm not going to leave you here all alone over the weekend."

"Scott, don't be a fool. I can't expect you to stay here with me. Your place is with your family now. Please."

"You will go crazy locked up in here all weekend."

"Stop worrying about me! You're going and that's that! You shouldn't have been here in the first place!" Anger now filled my words.

"Penney, my place is always with you. They will understand."

"No! I can't live with that! You have to go. Please," I begged him.

"Are you sure that you'll be all right here?"

"God. I'll be fine. It will give me time to catch up on some reading. Just go."

"Okay. I do want to be there. But . . . will you . . . ?"

"I'll be fine. You can call me as soon as you get there. Let me know how your mother is taking it. I'm sorry."

It did not occur to me that I might be able to leave with him. Later, when I thought about it, I pushed it out of my mind quickly. I could not go home, then return to 7-B. That would have been impossible for me. The children would never have understood. Everyone would see me the same way Helen had the previous night. They wouldn't have understood.

A part of me seemed to die that morning as I watched Scott drive away. I would have all weekend to dwell on what had happened that day. The only emotion I felt was guilt. Guilt for being in the Clinic. Guilt for forcing Scott to come up. Guilt for taking too long there. Guilt for being me.

DECEMBER 8, SATURDAY AFTERNOON

The Clinic was very quiet on weekends. As I walked through the West Clinic lobby, the emptiness created a feeling of unrest in me. All was still. Emptiness surrounded me. I felt right at home in this void. If only the world could be as easy to deal with as an empty room. But my mind continued to think despite my effort to forget. The same thoughts kept coming back at me. I had been a disappointment to everyone, including myself.

By the time I reached 7-B my mind was once again focused on Scott. Out of habit, I reached down and pressed the button on the door leading into 7-B. Not until the second attempt to gain entrance did I notice a young girl, short and slender, shoulder-length dark brown hair clinging to the pale green sweater she wore. She walked guardedly toward the door, never once taking her eyes from it. I pushed the button once again. There was no response from the other side, no buzz saying "come in." Once again I pressed the button. Once again I got no response.

Before I had a chance to ring again, two nurses rushed toward the girl. She was now directly in front of the door. Desperately she grabbed at the knob and turned it frantically as she tried to get out. One of the nurses said something to her as they approached her. Then they gently turned her around and walked her away from the door. Whatever it was that the nurse had said, it did the trick. It wasn't until they were halfway down the hall that I got the buzz to enter. Before I was through the door, the girl pushed the nurses away with all her might and ran frantically toward the door. She kept yelling, "Give me my baby! I want . . . my . . . B-A-B-Y!"

"Pull the door shut! Quickly!" one of the nurses yelled.

I grabbed the door and pulled the heavy metal door shut. The tone of their voices, loud and demanding, frightened me.

"Come on, Brenda, we will take you to your baby when you feel better. Just calm down and come with us." This time the nurse used more forceful measures to return her to her room.

The poor girl let out a bloodcurdling scream, "I WANT MY B-A-B-Y!" Her arms swung at the nurses as they dragged her into one of the rooms.

Not until later that day did I find out from one of the nurses on duty what had happened. She had given birth to a baby two weeks before. Everything had gone well until a few days before the incident, when she suddenly went insane. The nurse told me it was postpartum psychosis. I never knew anything like that could happen! It shook me up. Poor Brenda had to be put in restraints for the rest of the night, but that didn't stop her from crying out over and over that she wanted her baby. I was deeply moved by her plight.

DECEMBER 8, SATURDAY NIGHT

Saturday night, around dinner time, I found myself faced with another situation that would add to the guilt and uncertainties I was battling. Ralph, one of the nurses on the ward, joined Lizzy and me for dinner. Helen and Joyce were out on passes.

The cafeteria was much quieter on weekends. We had no difficulty finding a quiet corner to eat in. The meal started out with the usual conversation but soon moved into an area I was not prepared to deal with.

"I understand you used to be an X-ray technician, Penney. I'm a registered tech also. I do some work from time to time to pick up a few extra bucks. Why don't you work any more?" Ralph asked, as he put the last of his chile dog in his mouth.

"Because, Scott and I both feel it's important for me to stay home and be there for the kids," I replied.

"Yes, but is that enough? I mean, don't you feel like you should have something other than just a house and kids?" he asked.

"No. What do you mean something else? That is enough." And I thought to myself, Isn't it?

"A woman can never be too careful these days. What if something happened to your husband? What if he up and walked out on you?" Ralph's beady little eyes peered at me from across the table. "And what is wrong with earning a few extra bucks now? No one can convince me that being a housewife is fulfilling!"

"It is," I argued. Although the anger was building inside at his insinuations, I couldn't respond as I would have liked. Instead, I said, "I was happy doing what I did. As soon as I get the pain under control, everything will be all right." There was no emotion in my voice.

"No way. You aren't going to be happy unless you do something worthwhile, and house and kids are not it. My wife would go . . ."

"What the hell business is it of yours anyway?" Lizzy finally entered the conversation. "Why can't she do what she wants? It ain't no business of yours, turkey!" Lizzy shouted at him as she reached down for my arm. "Come on, let's get the hell away from this jerk!"

As I followed her out of the cafeteria I said, "Lizzy, thanks. I don't understand why he did that. God! I am falling apart!"

DECEMBER 9, SUNDAY

Sunday passed uneventfully, and I was hardly aware of time. The guilt about Scott just kept gnawing away at me.

DECEMBER 10, MONDAY MORNING

"Are you still here?" asked the cleaning lady who was standing just inside my doorway as I walked out of the bathroom Monday morning. She was an elderly, stout woman, disheveled from all the bending and stooping she did. Her remark affected me deeply. I realized I had been here so long that even the cleaning lady noticed and had to comment.

Joyce was in a good mood as she walked into group that morning. She was going home. Her husband was waiting for her. Admittedly, it was going home to the same life she had left, the same daily routine of taking care of her family. But she was happy anyway.

She was leaving, even though she had come after I had. She was apparently well enough to go home. I was feeling far too sorry for myself to share in her joy that morning. Why was I still there? Why were they letting her go home and keeping me?

"Is Dr. Covington keeping you here so long because you are that sick or that good looking?" asked a male nurse as I walked into the lounge for a cup of coffee. Although he may have meant it to be flattering, I was too depressed to be amused and did not need his remark.

It was a combination of everything that had happened since I found out about Scott's grandfather. No, it started even before that, with Helen's asking me why I was there. Everything I did or said seemed to go wrong. I had let Scott down when he needed me most. No one could understand why I was there so long, and they didn't hesitate to question me. Joyce's leaving before me just wasn't the way it was supposed to work. There were so many negative thoughts going around in my head, thoughts I didn't understand and feelings I didn't fully recognize, that I didn't have the energy to try to figure them out.

All I could see or feel was the despair. I was sure that nothing could help me now, and because of my stubbornness, I was both unwilling and unable to do anything about it. I was done fighting, done trying to help myself. I had tried and failed. It always came back to the same problem—me. So I resigned myself to a life of looking without seeing, touching without feeling, screaming without being heard, crying without tears.

Helen and Lizzy detected my mood change immediately. I refused to talk to either of them.

"Penney, you ready to go to dinner?" Lizzy asked, her voice uncertain. "Helen and I are waiting for you."

Without looking up at her, I shook my head.

"Come on. You got to eat something. You didn't go down to lunch. We'll drag you there if we have to."

"I'm not hungry! Let me be . . . please."

"Not until you go to dinner. Then you can sit here in this damn room and pout all damn night if you want to. But now you are coming with us!"

I agreed to go with them just to shut Lizzy up, but I ate nothing.

"Penney, come with me. Now!" Dr. Gabis stood in the doorway of my room. I knew from his stern tone he meant business.

Like a puppy who knew it had done something wrong, I followed him down the hall. He pushed the button and the door flung open. "Come on. Over here." He pointed to the door that led into our group room.

As we entered the room, he walked toward the desk and commanded, "Sit down."

There was a moment of silence. His eyes peered at me, his glare both frightening and sad. "You want to tell me what has been going on today!"

I turned my head away from him and sat silently.

"Penney, if you don't talk to me, how can I help you?"

Still no response from me. I could hear his words. I knew he was concerned about me. But I just could not respond.

"Penney, please!"

The room was dead, not a sound to be heard, except the steady tic tic tic on the wall. I wanted to cry out to him. I wanted him to reach me, help me break this silence that had somehow overtaken me. But I couldn't. Something inside me stopped the words from forming. I felt as if my body was there, sitting in the chair, but I was somewhere off in the distance, looking on. The words I wanted to say—*help me help me*—rolled through my mind, but I was silent.

"Penney . . . . You have come too far to give up now. Why don't you tell me what has happened so I can help you. You have always been willing to talk with me before. What is so wrong that you can't talk to me now?" He was pleading now.

The fear inside me swelled as his words echoed in my mind. I wanted him to keep trying. He couldn't give up on me now, but . . . I couldn't help him.

Twenty minutes of entreaties could not penetrate my silence. Dr. Gabis had to admit that despite his skill, compassion, and understanding he was not capable of pulling me out of this one. I could feel my will slipping away as I left the room where Dr. Gabis had tried so hard to rekindle my awareness of life. Nothing mattered to me. Only the unspoken words crying for help rang in my head.

Attempts by several other staff members became exercises in futility as I remained locked in my silence. I was now not only unwilling, but unable, to summon help. I stood in a distant place seeing and hearing all that went on, but I felt totally removed and inert. I watched myself hold fast to silence. I wanted to reach out and comfort my own being and make myself respond, but too many things had hurt me, too many of my actions had drawn me into a silence I could not break. It was too painful to face up to the truth.

DECEMBER 10, MONDAY EVENING

As each moment of silence passed, I became more aware of my state of mind. I felt that if something was not done soon, I might slip away and never come back, exist in an empty shell drained of all life. But I was still powerless to call out for help.

Stella! The last person I need to see! Get out of here . . . Get out of here!

She sat still and didn't attempt to break my silence. It was as if she was trying to absorb what I felt. She seemed to be waiting for just the right moment. I could feel her looking at me. I knew she would not remain still for long. I tried desperately to block her presence from my mind and hold fast to my silence.

But I had reached the end of my endurance, and I was overcome by a need to reach out to Stella. As she began talking softly to me, I heard the words, and I felt them. I could feel my resistance weaken. My desire to release the feelings that had festered inside me for three days filtered slowly into my consciousness. Stella expressed her genuine sadness because of my setback, and her desire to see me make it. Whatever had kept me going all those years with the pain, once again emerged in me. I knew I did not want to fall inside myself, lost forever. I wanted to feel, even if the feelings were painful. I needed to respond.

Stella's words began to break through my thoughts as I became increasingly aware of the force and control needed to remain so removed. My chin began to quiver as Stella reached out to touch my hand. Her hand was warm. I felt the warmth softly spread throughout my body, melting my heart, which had felt like ice. It was the soft touch that stirred up the warmth of life itself. That touch put the first crack in a wall built to prevent just such things from reaching me, to prevent any more hurt from filling my mind.

Tears streamed down my face as my body came alive again. Uncontrollable tears that I had locked inside washed away much of the tension I had placed on myself, tears of both sadness and joy.

"Oh, Ste . . . lla . . . I have let Scott . . . down. Heeeee . . . need . . . ed me."

I tried my best to get words out to express my feelings. "Why did all this have to happen? I really tried, but . . . but . . . there were just so many things that happened, I couldn't handle all of them."

Stella did not try to answer. She allowed me to sit there and free myself of all the burdens I had been carrying around. With her gentle grip still embracing my hand, I began to gain insight into what had happened to me.

My biggest problem was allowing feelings to build up, avoiding confrontations with people, as I had with Helen over the remark she'd made to me. Unable to justify my reason for being there and doubting my own self-worth, I withdrew into myself. I blocked out what I thought was impossible to handle. I was much too sensitive to what was said.

As my tears vanished, so did my silence. I began to feel alive again. I felt my lungs fill with air and saw the faint lights illuminating the room. I heard the sounds outside my own head and became aware of my body. I wanted to live again and to understand what had happened. I felt the relief of knowing I had been saved from emotions that had almost destroyed me.

"You know, I kept asking myself over and over again why I was here. I really thought I didn't have any right to be here. Helen instilled such guilt in me. But it was guilt I was already feeling. Guilt I felt the day I walked in here knowing I was not fulfilling my role as a mother and wife. Guilt I had about being here so long. Most of all it was guilt I felt because of my lack of interest in my own children and husband. God, a person can certainly lose track of reality." I quickly reviewed the previous few days, examining all the feelings I had denied.

I realized that I had clung to old hurts. "Does anyone ever get over all the things that happen to them? You know, feeling inadequate about yourself. Feeling as if you always have to think of the other guy first. Is it possible to see yourself as good, one who people like just because you are who you are?"

Stella replied, "You know you can't please everyone. No matter how hard you try, someone is not going to like what you do or say." Then she opened up to me for the first time. "I had a hard time with that once. I tried to please too many people too often, and it got the better of me. It was a painful lesson to realize that I had to like myself and please myself first." As she spoke I could see that she knew more than I had realized. She just might have understood all along what I was going through. I had misjudged her and had prevented her from helping me.

All the people I had blamed for my own failures now seemed unimportant. And everything else that had happened during the day seemed equally unimportant. I saw how I had grabbed on to what people said and how I twisted and distorted things.

I could see that I had tried much too hard to find answers that were not necessary. I had pretended, as I had done all my life, that nothing could get me down. It had started as an attempt to gain my parents' love, love I felt I didn't have. I had from those early years on allowed feelings to build up inside, which made it almost impossible for me to deal effectively with my life. Most important, I realized that this self-recognition was but the very first step, that I could now start to help myself. I began to understand that life was not black and white, but a rainbow of magnificent colors and that there were usually many things to take into account before passing judgment on someone else, or even on myself.

I can remember telling Dr. Gabis, when he was questioning me about what I would do when I left the Clinic, that I wanted to be good at just one thing. I wanted to be better than anyone else in a skill, to feel I had some worth or something special to offer. That is where I got hung up: searching for something I had all along. In looking for something that would help me conceal my low self-esteem, I had overlooked myself. No one could be better at being me than me.

That night, with Stella's understanding and love, I made much progress. I had experienced the depths of despair and saw how destructive it could be. I knew I had a long way to go to achieve complete awareness and understanding, but at least now I was willing to try. My wall came tumbling down as I sat there enjoying Stella's company for hours on end.

DECEMBER 11, TUESDAY

"So, I hear you're feeling much better. I was really worried about you yesterday," Dr. Gabis said.

"I was worried about me yesterday, too. I can't say that I understand all that has happened, but I am sure going to go slower this time."

"It's important for you to understand that your pain is a true physical one. The fibrositis is caused by certain irregularities in your body. While you were pregnant, your body produced more cortisone, which kept the progress of pain in check during that time. You did say you had some discomfort before your pregnancy, didn't you?'' Dr. Gabis asked, his tone now one of a professional.

"Yes. I had noticed my right leg was achy, and I had had those awful headaches right before I found out I was pregnant." I thought a moment, needing to have a better understanding of what I could expect down the road. This was the first time in weeks that I had had the opportunity to question anyone about my physical well-being. "Then I guess what you are saying is that I really had this problem before I had Scotty. Once I delivered . . . it got worse?''

"You could say that. Everyone's body is different and reacts differently to situations. It's a pretty good certainty that you did have fibrositis before Scotty. And I bet you felt the pain, you just didn't do anything about it. Your need to perform was much greater than the pain," he said, looking directly at me.

"I guess I did push myself a little," I said as my eyes rolled up toward the ceiling in a sign of exaggeration. "I hope that now I can make better use of my time. For the important things—Scott and the kids."

"Just remember that your stress level will contribute greatly to the amount of pain you experience in the future. We'll keep you on the Elavil and see how you do. That will help you to reach deep sleep at night. Most people with fibrositis aren't able to achieve a deep level of sleep, so they always wake up tired and stiff. The Elavil should correct your sleep disturbance and solve part of your pain problem. Just don't start denying your feelings to yourself. Try to be more aware of your own needs and realize they are just as important as anyone else's." Dr. Gabis stopped for a moment, glancing out the window before continuing. "Do you have the answer to my question yet? What are you going to do after you leave the Clinic?''

"I've given that a lot of thought today. You know what? I'm not going to do anything. Not right away. I'm just going

to enjoy being myself and being with my family. And I'm
going to give myself another chance to get to know my parents,
Be on the same level with them rather than putting myself
beneath them. I think they do love me; I just didn't love myself
enough for their love to penetrate my negative thoughts. I
can't help but think I missed out on a lot in the frame of mind
I was in for so long." I paused a moment. "Nope, I am just
going to take it easy for a while. Maybe, when I feel it's right
for me, I'll look for something else. For now, I just want to
appreciate life."

I expected Dr. Gabis to try one more time to convince me
to do something more constructive with my life, but he didn't.
He was perfectly happy knowing I had made a decision about
what I felt was right for me. He didn't really feel strongly about
my going to school. If I felt that was what I wanted, it was
fine with him. I think in retrospect, that they often posed questions to me just to get me thinking for myself about what was
right, without all my old values coming into play. What I saw
as a threat or a conspiracy to change me was just an attempt
to get me to examine and understand my own wants and needs
carefully so I could make the right decisions.

The rest of our talk that day was spent in pleasant conversation about the future. That day my future looked great!

The days grew longer and I felt the need to leave; I had
finally won the war. My love for my children and Scott were
restored. Affections I had denied myself I was now free to feel.
The gentleness and innocence of the children I had almost
lost, softly embraced my thoughts. The love I could now share
with them intensified with each precious memory of them.

My soul was filled with love for Scott and I no longer
hesitated to express it. My detachment from him had not been
from lack of love, but rather the fear of being hurt. Looking
back on those seven weeks, I realized just how much I had
learned, not only about myself but about Scott as well. I knew
that Scott would not have stood by me if he had not indeed

loved me. I had a lot to discover, and I was excited about my life.

DECEMBER 12, WEDNESDAY

The gynecologist, after examining me, felt I should have a D & C done before making a final determination as to the cause of my pain. I scheduled the procedure for the end of January to allow myself some time to enjoy my freedom. The last thing in the world I wanted was to be placed back in the role of a patient.

The D & C revealed that my uterus was tipped back just enough to create some discomfort during intercourse. There were no other irregularities found.

DECEMBER 13, THURSDAY

It seemed almost unreal. I never thought the day would come, that I'd be leaving 7-B feeling so good. I was filled with excitement. Plans for the future ran through my head. I knew, without a doubt, that I was ready to go home. I was no longer afraid to face the world.

I felt confident I could act and feel like an adult around my parents and see them from an entirely different perspective, one of understanding, and love. I knew that they had done the best they could for me and that it was only my repressed anger toward them and myself that had created so many doubts in my mind. They were not my enemies, and I hoped they could become my friends and allies. I planned to start anew with them when I returned home, to really, for the first time in my life, get to know them. All the old hurts that had surfaced during my time on 7-B, were now in perspective. I did not have to hold on to those hurtful memories to avoid the chance of getting hurt. I had recognized them, understood them for what they were, dealt with them, and, most important let them go. I was ready to start a new life, one I felt certain I could accept.

I finished what I could of the packing and walked over to the window to look down on the street. I had seen the same street many times before. I remember the way I used to feel, empty, cold, and alone, as I would watch the cars pass, always wondering where all those people were off to, and why they wanted to go in the first place. As I gazed onto the street, I became excited knowing that soon I would join all those people with someplace to go. I knew how much there was to be had out in the world and I was determined to experience as much as possible. Now, I wanted to be free of 7-B, a place I had been more than happy to remain for seven long weeks, a place of refuge. But as each minute passed and I was getting closer to the end of my stay, I wanted to leave. I needed to fill my life again with the people I loved. It didn't seem possible that I could have stayed there so long without once feeling the way I did right then: alive.

Morning could not come fast enough. I closed my suitcase and waited for the long, endless night to pass. Life awaited me just around the corner.

DECEMBER 14, FRIDAY

The day finally arrived. The sun filled the room with a soft winter light. December fourteenth—forty-four days since I first set foot in that room. They were long, endless days, but they had finally paid off.

I wasn't the only one of our group to leave that day— Lizzy, Helen, and I would make our exodus together. Just a few more hours and we would all be on our way.

Stella said her good-byes to me. She was the one person I had misunderstood from the beginning; now I would miss her. She had been there when I needed her. In her own way and time, she had proved to be one of my greatest allies. As she embraced me, speaking soft words of encouragement, I realized what she meant to me.

Saying good-bye to the group was not an easy task either. It seemed as if we had been together for years. Our unique friendship, I felt certain, would endure. We shed a few tears as we promised to keep in touch.

There were no words to express my gratitude to Dr. Covington and Dr. Gabis. They had given me new life, standing beside me all the way, never allowing me to give up on myself. They used all their skill to direct and guide me to a greater understanding of myself. I felt inadequate as I said my final good-byes to them. I wanted to hand them the world on a silver platter. Wishing them the best that life could offer, I walked out the door. I became a free person for the first time in weeks, maybe for the first time in my life. It was the end of the Clinic, but just the beginning for me.

EPILOGUE

Eleven years have passed since I walked out of the Clinic. They have had both good and bad in them, but for all eleven years I have remained a vital human being. I left the patient's role behind me and continued my life as a person. I have allowed myself to feel, to recognize emotions and to deal with them rather than tucking them away in my mind where they would fester until I was forced to deal with them. I have allowed myself to make mistakes, to accept both the good and bad sides of my personality. I am no longer trying to be something I am not and never will be. I have put aside my pain behavior and become more assertive.

Nothing is ever black or white. My parents, although I felt they were partly responsible for the way I was, did what they felt was in my best interest. It was my personality that allowed all the confusion and contradiction of my childhood to rule my adult life, making it all but impossible to make realistic decisions. In the past eleven years I have become very close to them. My father has passed away, but I did get the chance to let him know I love him before he died. My mother has become a very important part of my life, a friend. I've learn that it's okay for me to love them in spite of negative feelings. We all have negative—and positive—feelings about the people we love.

I know I can only do as much for my children—allow them to be who they are—and hope they will be strong enough to do so. All I can really give my children is the ability to accept who they are and not to be afraid to show their feelings. If my children leave home to make their own lives with a high self-esteem, then I have succeeded.

My era of pain is over, and I've learned a great deal from it. It provided me with a golden opportunity to understand myself better. I now do my best to take responsibility for my own actions, and I no longer feel I have to explain myself to everyone.

The stretching exercises are still a part of my life. I know I must do them every day to maintain muscle tone and strength. But it is a small price to pay. I look at exercise as a positive thing I do for myself to start the day. I am still taking the Elavil I was on during my stay at the Clinic. It has been very effective in helping me to maintain my own wellness.

I have been able to keep my head above water. My experience at the Clinic not only helped me deal with pain, but showed me that even without the pain, my life would have eventually gone downhill had I not gotten help. My outlook on life is, in general, much more positive. I do not put as many conditions on my behavior. It is nice to let people know who I am and to be respected not only by others, but by myself. It feels good to be free to be me.

Dr. Covington had talked several times about a support group for people like myself who have to deal with chronic pain. Not a group that would focus on pain, but one that would work from positives pain management skills to put their pain in perspective, and help its members to leave their roles as patients and become whole. After giving his idea much thought, I decided to start one, which I did in 1980.

We can't take anyone's pain away. Not even Dr. Covington could do that. What our group does is give support and direction to those who want to help themselves deal with day-to-day pain. We share with our members some of the same tools that the Clinic taught me. The group, American Chronic Pain Association, Inc., is working—often slowly, but it is working. People have discovered they are not alone in their war against pain, that their feelings are not as unusual as they thought. They learn that the people in group really care. It is such a beautiful thing to watch such caring grow over the weeks and to see people put their pain into perspective, to see members begin to operate from a positive stance, to see them accept that anything is possible.

We all have a right to full and happy lives. Although our backgrounds are different, and we all see things in a different way, we still need the support and caring of others. Sometimes families can't supply that caring because they may be too willing to allow us to remain patients for the rest of our lives. It is difficult to sit back and watch someone struggling to take those first few steps going from the patient role to the person role by becoming involved in their own recovery, but the group can offer many stepping-stones to walk on. Don't we all deserve a little understanding and direction? Whatever the problem may be, whether it is physical pain or emotional pain, don't we owe it to ourselves to try? I think we do.

I am more aware of life and what is going on around me now. I am not so quick to judge others, or myself for that matter. I accept some things for what they are, knowing there is nothing I can do to change them. But I am not afraid to challenge others that I know I can overcome if given time.

The number of self-help, mutual-aid groups across the country is countless. No matter what the problem, there is a group that can meet your needs. But remember, self-help means just that. You must be willing to help yourself first. All the love and caring is useless unless you take the first step. I had the good fortune of not only taking the first step, but being directed, understood, cared for, and loved along the way. There is hope for every one of us!

If you are interested in finding more about the American Chronic Pain Association, you can call the national office at (916) 632-0922. At present there are over five hundred chapters in the United States, Canada, Australia, and New Zealand to help you.

My involvement with the American Chronic Pain Association has helped keep me well. I do not know where I would be, eleven years after leaving the Clinic, if it had not been for group. Giving members and leaders positive reinforcement, is a way of reminding myself of all I must do to maintain my own health. It is something I must work at constantly, but it is worth the effort. I am worth the effort.

APPENDIX I

Ten Concepts:
Moving From Patient to Person

FIRST, ACCEPTANCE OF THE PAIN

At first you will look to the medical community to take away your pain. The weeks and months that follow are filled with mixed emotions and confusion. At some point you will realize that you are living with chronic pain. The phrase "learn to live with it" becomes all too familiar to you. While the ACPA dose not replace proper medical treatment, we can help you work along with your medical program in "learning to live with it."

SECOND: GETTING INVOLVED

Now that you have accepted the fact that you do indeed have chronic pain, it is important that you realize that you must become actively involved in your own recovery. Attending your first ACPA meeting is a good beginning. If you are unable to attend an ACPA meeting, follow the suggestions set forth here.

THIRD: PRIORITIES

What is the most important thing to you today? You must

ask yourself this question each day. It is helpful to keep a list of things you feel are important in your life. This list should include not only problems but also things that make you happy and things that you must address. The purpose of setting priorities is to realize that nothing is absolutely black and white, including your life. You must be flexible and learn to focus on your life instead of on your pain. Setting your priorities helps you to find the starting point to begin to move back into the mainstream of active life.

FOURTH: REALISTIC GOALS

By recognizing your limitations and knowing your priorities, you can begin to set specific goals for yourself. In the past, your pain has probably stopped you from performing many of your usual activities. You may have shut yourself off from the outside world. As each day begins, you cannot find a good reason to get out of bed. Having a goal will provide you with a reason. Goals do not have to be centered on work but rather on activities that you enjoy. Setting aside relaxation time can be a realistic goal. Accomplishing one of your goals is a powerful force in generating a positive attitude and helping you to learn to live with pain. After many successes, anything is possible.

FIFTH: YOUR BASIC RIGHTS

No matter who you are, what you look like, or what you do, you have certain basic rights. These rights establish the fundamental principles of your actions and reactions. It is important that you study these rights, understand them, and use them in your daily life. These rights will give you freedom to explore vast opportunities that you may not have believed possible before. Your rights will allow you to be you without feeling guilty.

SIXTH: RECOGNIZING EMOTIONS

Your body and mind are one. Many people feel that their pain is only in their bodies. Others are afraid that it is all in their heads. Both are half right. Pain affects both the mind and body. It is impossible to separate your physical sensations from your emotional ones. Certain cycles occur during emotional highs and lows. When you are happy you laugh, and the entire body seems to experience this happiness. When you are sad your body feels weighed down and heavy. The emotional self directly affects your physical well-being. Anxiety causes you to tense up all over. Every muscle in your body will contract, and sore muscles will ache even more. What you experience in everyday life has a bearing on your degree of pain. You must begin to recognize your emotions, understand them, and deal with them. Any unsolved emotion will have some effect on your pain level. With the help and support of the group, you can sort through some issues that you may have been afraid of before.

SEVENTH: RELAXATION

You can learn to control, to some degree, how your body feels. By practicing the relaxation techniques used in group meetings, you can tell your body how you want it to feel. Learning relaxation exercises does take practice. When you have mastered them, you will know that, indeed, you can learn to live with your pain.

EIGHTH: EXERCISE

It is common for individuals with chronic pain to become physically unfit by avoiding actions or exercises that may have temporarily increased their pain. It is to your benefit to begin to regain control over your body. After following a regular program of mild stretching exercises (**which your doctor must ap-**

prove), you will notice that your pain level may have decreased. Good muscle tone will decrease the amount of pain you feel.

NINTH: TOTAL OUTLOOK

Reviewing all of the previous concepts, you can see exactly how your life has improved with each new step. Realize that you are now in control of your life once again. Share your experience with the group, especially the new members.

TENTH: OUTREACH

It is estimated that one in every three persons suffers from some form of chronic pain. Many of these people still manage to function in spite of the pain. Many others will slowly withdraw into their own world. This is a world with which you are familiar. Share what you have learned with others. Contact a new member and help him or her through the steps you have just accomplished. Learning to live with pain is an ongoing experience, and while you are helping another, you will be reinforcing yourself.

Establish contact with a local pain unit and arrange a convenient time for you to visit. Your visit can be a tremendous help to those who are just starting on their long road to recovery. Individuals who are scheduled to be discharged from a pain unit are afraid of the outside world. Let them know about the ACPA and how it can help them through its ongoing support.

Reprinted with the permission of the American Chronic Pain Association.

APPENDIX II

Guidelines to Help Select a Pain Unit

Many who suffer from chronic pain have been through a number of different treatments. They have tried physical therapy, biofeedback, surgery, medications, counseling, and other treatment modalities without much success. They find that the pain affects virtually every aspect of their everyday lives: work, home, school, and social activities are all controlled by the pain.

If you want to regain control of your life, it is important that you learn how to cope with chronic pain. Although your pain may never go away, it is possible to reduce pain levels and, more important, to improve the quality of your life. To do so, you may need a multidisciplinary approach to chronic pain. While many of you may have tried almost every available medical intervention without great success, sometimes these therapies are most effective when performed together in a controlled setting. To successfully regain control of your life, you must have all the necessary ingredients of pain management in the right quantity. *It is possible to live with chronic pain.*

A multidisciplinary pain program can provide you with the necessary skills, medical intervention, and direction to effectively cope with chronic pain. The following information will tell you how to go about locating a pain management program in your area, what to look for in a well defined pain program, and what other issues to consider.

MULTIDISCIPLINARY PAIN MANAGEMENT UNITS:

Make sure you locate a legitimate program

* Hospitals and rehabilitation centers are more likely to offer comprehensive treatment than are "stand alone" programs.
* Facilities that offer pain management should include several specific components, listed below.
* The Commission on Accreditation of Rehabilitation Facilities [telephone: (602) 748-1212] can provide you with a listing of accredited pain programs in your area (your health insurance may require that the unit be CARF accredited in order for you to receive reimbursement). You can also contact the American Pain Society, a group of health care providers, at (708) 966-5595 for additional information about pain units in your area.

Choose a good program that is convenient
for you and your family

* Most pain management programs are part of a hospital or rehabilitation center. The program should be housed in a separate unit designed for pain management.
* Many pain management programs do not offer inpatient care. Choosing a program close to your home will enable you to commute to the program each day.

Learn something about the people who run the program

* Try to meet several of the staff members to get a sense of the people you will be dealing with while on the unit.

* The program should have a complete medical staff trained in pain management techniques including:
Physician (may be a neurologist, psychiatrist, physiatrist, or anesthesiologist, but should have expertise in pain management)
Registered nurse
Psychiatrist or psychologist
Physical therapist
Occupational therapist
Biofeedback therapist
Family counselor
Vocational counselor
Personnel trained in pain management intervention

Make sure the program includes most of the following features

* Biofeedback training
* Group therapy
* Counseling
* TENS units
* Regional anesthesia (nerve blocks)
* Physical therapy (exercise and body mechanics training, not massage, whirlpool, etc.)
* Relaxation training and stress management
* Educational program covering medications and other aspects of pain and its management
* Aftercare (follow-up support once you have left the unit)

* Occupational therapy
* Family counseling
* Assertiveness training

Be sure your family can be involved in your care

* Family members should be required to be involved in your treatment.
* The program should provide special educational sessions for family members.
* Joint counseling for you and your family should also be available.

Also consider these additional factors

* What services will your insurance company reimburse, and what will you be expected to cover?
* What is the unit's physical set-up (is it in a patient care area or in an area by itself)?
* What is the program's length of stay?
* Is the program inpatient or outpatient (when going through medication detoxification, inpatient care is recommended)
* If you choose an out-of-town unit, can your family be involved in your care?
* Do you understand what will be required of you during your stay (length of time you will be on unit, responsibility to take care of personal needs, etc.)?
* Does the unit provide any type of job retraining?
* Make sure that, before accepting you, the unit reviews your previous medical records and gives you a complete physical evaluation to be sure you can participate in the program.
* Your personal physician can refer you to the unit, but many programs also accept self-referral.
* Obtain copies of your recent medical records to prevent duplicate testing.
* Before you enter the unit, check with your insurance company to see what type of benefits it provides for pain management.
* Try to talk with both present and past program participants to get their feedback about their stay on the unit.

Pain management can make a significant difference in your life; however, you must realize that much of what you gain from your stay will be up to you. Treatment is designed to help you get out of the patient role and back to being a person. The program should help to restore your ability to function and to enjoy life. It will be up to you to become actively involved in the program if you expect to regain control of your life. Pain programs are difficult, but the benefits can improve your lifestyle!

If you need further information, please feel free to contact the American Chronic Pain Association's national office at P.O. Box 850, Rocklin, CA 95677, (916) 632-0922.

Reprinted with the permission of the American Chronic Pain Association.